ESCAPE FROM ALCOHOL

Escape From Alcohol

by
DONALD W.
HEWITT, M.D.

PACIFIC PRESS PUBLISHING ASSOCIATION

MOUNTAIN VIEW, CALIFORNIA

Brookfield, Illinois   Cristobal, Canal Zone   Portland, Oregon   Omaha, Nebraska

Library of Congress Catalog Card Number
53-6430

Copyright, 1953, by
Pacific Press Publishing Association

FOREWORD

The author first became interested in the problem of alcoholism and its treatment some seventeen years ago while serving an internship and residency in psychiatry. He subsequently entered private practice in Honolulu, Hawaii, where he maintained an office within a stone's throw of famed Waikiki Beach. His interest in the alcoholic and his plight medically, sociologically, and spiritually, continued unabated; and in a few years' time the author found himself conducting a charity alcoholic rehabilitation clinic, to which came many of the "low-bottom" alcoholics from Honolulu's skid row around Aala Park.

From continued contact with these unfortunates and from a study of the disheartening similarity of their stories of the failure of medical and psychiatric hospitalization, and every other conceivable type of alcoholic therapy to effect a permanent cure in their cases, the author became convinced that the only sure and lasting cure for alcoholism lay in a spiritual approach to the problem.

In the following pages of this book he cites a few of the many alcoholic cases that have come to his attention in the past fifteen years. Some of these examples are from the lower-class group of society, but not all. Alcoholism knows no class lines. There are many men and women on skid row who have college degrees; who have known riches, luxury, and even political and economic power.

The author wishes that all who read these pages will note that each year of clinical work has only increased his certain knowledge that the ones who have stopped "trying" to overcome alcoholism and, instead, have turned their problem in its entirety over to God for solution, have achieved peace, sobriety, serenity, and happiness such as they would never have previously imagined to be possible.

And he proves, just as conclusively, that the alcoholic who stubbornly clings to the belief that he himself or some other human agency can do this for him, is foredoomed to failure and to a lifetime of progressively intensifying alcoholic misery and degradation.

The author is now practicing in Los Angeles, where he is continuing his rehabilitation work with alcoholics as the chief medical advisor of a charity alcoholic clinic for men, located on the city's skid row, and a similar unit for women situated some miles west of it.

THE PUBLISHERS.

CONTENTS

Chapter 1

Hairpin Turn

"OPEN up in there! This is the law!"

The ominous words filtered through the befogged consciousness of the unshaven, haggard man lying on the bed. With a tremendous effort he tried to shake himself free of the benumbing codeine he had taken only a few minutes before.

"Open up in there or we're coming in!"

The man on the bed made a convulsive heave and finally succeeded in half falling, half staggering onto the floor. As he did so the door to the room gave way with a splintering crash and two burly men in civilian dress burst in. That they were plain-clothes men was written all over them. The bedraggled occupant of the room with a shrill animal cry moved in the direction of the window, but the leader of the two held his arm in a viselike grip and tossed him roughly back on the bed.

"Where's the stuff?" the leader rasped harshly. "You'd better come clean, pop, or we'll give you a rough way to go!"

"Wha-a-a-t stuff?" his hapless victim quavered helplessly from his recumbent position on the bed.

"Listen, pop, I just got through tellin'—"

"Hold on a second, Bill!" It was the second man speaking. While the stark drama on the bed had been taking place, he had been rummaging around the room. He now returned from the shabby dresser that was one of the room's few articles of furniture. He waved a piece of paper toward his confederate. "Somethin's haywire here, Bill," he said. "This old geezer was getting ready to bump himself off. Read this suicide note."

Bill took the proffered paper and read it intently. "Well, I'll be—," he exclaimed when he had finished. "We surely have the wrong steer by the tail, Ed. But how come? This is room 424, isn't it? That's where that marijuana was supposed to be cached, wasn't it? This has me licked, no fooling."

"Yeah, this is room 424, all right," Ed said slowly; "but, listen, chum, we were supposed to go to 324 on the third floor. Remember? So run down and see what's cooking there while I see what it's all about here, will you? Looks as if we got the wrong floor."

When Bill had left, Ed turned to the pitiful figure quivering on the bed.

"All right, pop, what's this all about?" he asked in a not unkindly voice. "What made you decide to take a trip into the unknown, as the writers say?"

The tension and strain of the past few minutes had taken their toll of the broken old man on the bed. In a toneless voice that sometimes quavered he recited the sordid and common story of a life that uncontrolled drinking had gradually captured, of a faithful wife who had borne all his drunken eccentricities she could, of senseless spending sprees that had left his family virtually penniless, and all of the other familiar alcoholic antics that differ only in detail, yet which, in their composite pattern, bear a striking resemblance.

Ed listened to the old man's tale with the worldly wisdom born of some fifteen years of service with the Los Angeles Police Department, during which he had run across about everything on the seamy side of life. At last, when the old man's voice trailed off in nothingness and he seemed about to relapse into a semicomatose condition, he spoke.

"Now take it easy, old-timer, and we'll see if we can't work out some solution to your troubles. I know you're feeling pretty rough, but a few days in the general hospital should take care of that."

The old man was suddenly galvanized into life. "No, no, anything but that!" he almost shrieked. "That's what my stepson wanted to do with me, and I've had all I want of 'psycho' wards!"

"Oh, so that's it, is it?" Ed mused. "Now I'm beginning to see daylight. Well, what do you think we should do, old-timer? We can't leave you here, you know. Is there any place other than a hospital where someone will take care of you?"

"Yes, there is," the old man replied. "Some time ago I met a doctor at a charity alcoholic clinic located on East Fourth Street. He told me that if I ever needed help with my drinking problem to look him up."

"Well, believe me, that time is now," Ed remarked grimly. "What's the exact address? I'll see to it that you get there."

The old man's brows knitted in a worried frown. "Lemme see," he began hesitantly. "Was it 225? No, I think it was 335, or maybe—" The voice gradually trailed off again as he strove to fight the advancing codeine-induced coma that was slowly but surely gaining ground. With a sigh of utter weariness, his head dropped back on the pillow and he lapsed into insensibility.

"Well, the old man is in never-never land for sure now," mused Ed, surveying the unconscious, recumbent form with a look that strangely belied his role of a tough police officer.

At that moment Bill returned with a disgusted look on his face. "Our bird flew the coop," he announced briefly, throwing his hat savagely on the top of the dresser; "and, believe me, we'd better keep it quiet about knocking off the wrong room, or we'll both be pounding a beat. What's the matter?" he ended suddenly, indicating his interest in the inert form of the old man on the bed with an inquiring jerk of his thumb. "Looks as if pop is catching up with his beauty sleep."

Ed had been listening to Bill's comments with a worried frown on his face. Then he spoke suddenly.

"We'll play dumb about the whole deal," he said, "and nobody'll be the wiser. But we have to do something about the old gent here, and the quicker the better. We can't have any corpus delicti around as evidence, you know," he added, with a wink at his companion. "So be a good boy, Bill, and get on the phone to see if you can find the address of this alcoholic rehabilitation clinic the old man mentioned. I know it's somewhere on East Fourth Street, and it shouldn't be too hard to locate."

In a few minutes Bill was in possession of the required information and an ambulance had been summoned.

Soon afterward I had my first glimpse of Thomas Richards. Identification could be established only through cards found in his possession, since he remained in a coma. I could see from a look at his ashen face and from checking his irregular, thready pulse that he was under heavy sedation of some description. There was no smell of alcohol present, so I ordered his stomach pumped out and prescribed other medication. Then I left instructions that I was to be called in the event there was a change for the worse in my patient's condition.

The next morning, on my daily visit to the clinic, I found Richards conscious, but in a very weak condition. Obviously he was suffering from acute malnutrition that had resulted from prolonged drinking without adequate food, and from the effects on mind and body of the alcohol itself.

For almost a week Richards hovered between life and death, with alternate periods of lucidity and delirium. But eventually an iron constitution, plus God's inscrutable plan for mankind in general and for Thomas Richards in particular, weighed the scales in favor of life.

At the first opportunity I talked to Richards concerning his alcoholic problem and the reasons why he should give himself over completely to God as the only chance to solve it.

"Yes, I know that God can do miracles, doctor," he replied earnestly; "that's already been proved by the fact that those two policemen broke into the wrong room in time to save me from suicide. But, honestly, doctor, I've led such a selfish, rotten life that I don't think God wants anything to do with me."

"That's where you're wrong, Tom," I replied. "The Bible says, 'Though your sins be as scarlet, they shall be as white as snow.' That's God's wonderful promise to sinners, and the only stipulation He makes is that we sincerely repent of our mistakes and ask for forgiveness."

It was something to see Tom's face lighted with renewed hope. "Doctor, if I could only believe that, I'd have some reason for going on living."

"Tom, you *can* believe it, if you only will."

The alcoholic ward was well supplied with Christian literature aimed at bringing the patients to a better understanding of God and into a closer relationship with Him. Tom had read *David Dare, Your Home and Health, Steps to Christ, The Desire of Ages,* and other evangelical material, and it was amazing to watch his spiritual progress. Previous experience had amply proved to me that the books mentioned are invaluable steppingstones in the alcoholic's approach to an understanding of the greatest book ever written, the Bible.

As Tom's religious education progressed, his whole being seemed to reach out like a parched plant on the desert for life-giving water. One day, as we were having our usual Bible discussion, I asked him for the story of his life, if he cared to give it to me.

"Well, doctor, as I said once before, it's not a pretty picture, believe me. But now that I have faith that God has forgiven my mistakes, perhaps it would relieve my mind and conscience to unburden myself. Where do you want me to begin?"

"I can think of no better place than the beginning," I replied with a smile.

"All right, doctor, you asked for it," he answered with a grin. "I was born in Chicago in 1888,—February 29th of that year to be exact,—and when I was only seven years old I was often sent by my father to the corner saloon to bring him a bucket of beer. My father, I might say right here, was a heavy drinker and quite probably an alcoholic, although we didn't use that term in those days.

"On these excursions I got in the habit of sneaking a few tastes of the foaming brew, and soon I acquired a liking for it. However, I never took enough to become intoxicated, but I do think it significant that the taste for alcohol, acquired at that age, stayed with me the rest of my life—that is, up until now," he added, with a confident, happy smile.

"At the age of eleven I was singing in the Episcopal church choir in the neighborhood, and when I was fifteen I became an altar boy. In this same year I went to work at my first job as a cashboy in Marshall Field's department store at the munificent salary of $3 a week. A cashboy, I should explain, was simply a boy who returned a customer's change after a purchase had been made. Nowadays, of course, this is done by containers shot through vacuum tubes or by other methods.

"My next jobs were with the Chicago, Burlington, and Quincy Railroad and the Pennsylvania Railroad. By this time I was seventeen years old, and I thought I had really reached manhood at last. In order to prove my maturity, I began going to roadhouse parties, where the favorite drink served was wine. One day, as I was playing pool

2—E.A.

with a friend in a combination poolroom and bar, we decided that we would try something stronger. We ordered whisky and, as the custom was in those days, the bartender placed the bottle on the bar and then left us to help ourselves. Of course, we were supposed to pay for each drink; but, while the bartender's attention was occupied elsewhere at the bar, we sneaked several extras. The result was that, not long afterward, I mounted a table, took off my coat, and challenged anyone in the place to a fight. Events that followed are hazy, but I was told later that I was fished out of the gutter by a detective friend of my sister's who happened to be passing that way and recognized me. This good Samaritan took me home, propped me up against the front door, rang the doorbell, and then prudently beat a retreat. When the door was opened a few seconds later by my mother, I literally fell into the house. Tears, recriminations, remorse, and fervent promises never to take another drink followed. This was in 1909.

"The following year I was married, and for about a year I did little drinking except for an occasional bottle of beer shared with my wife. I obtained a position with Foreman Brothers Banking Company and eventually rose to the position of assistant auditor. I remained there about six years and frequently got drunk at parties or on Saturday night; but my alcoholism had not as yet progressed to the point where liquor had become a daily necessity.

"When I was about twenty-eight years old I switched jobs and went over to S. B. Chapin and Company as a bookkeeper. Chapin's was a stock and bond organization and therefore supposed to expect decorous behavior from its employees. But my behavior, under the baneful influence of my growing thirst for alcohol, was becoming anything but decorous. One day the switchboard girl overheard me calling a race-track bookmaker to place a bet. She informed the boss, and when the latter called me on the carpet and questioned me regarding the matter, I admitted my guilt and was promptly fired.

"I went right across the street to another stock and bond firm and was hired as auditor. I started playing the stock market and ran a shoestring investment of $1,800 up into what constituted a fortune in those days—some $90,000. This was in 1926, and I was riding the crest of the wave. I owned a $25,000 home, two Packard automobiles, and I was a member of several exclusive clubs. I had a devoted wife and two children.

"Then came the disastrous stock-market crash of 1929, and my whole flimsy world collapsed around my ears. I lost everything, including my wife and children. My first reaction to this catastrophe was typically that of the alcoholic. I intensified my drinking and the all-night partying that had caused my wife to leave me. I became a drifter, and for the next two years I wandered aimlessly from city to city, never lasting long at any job, never satisfied with my lot, always dreaming of the past.

"In 1933 I found myself in Los Angeles, where I met a man named Lucas, who was operating a school of music. He hired me as a teacher of dramatic art and diction, and while thus engaged I met the woman who is my present wife. We were married in 1935, and shortly afterward the music school closed its doors because of lack of finances.

Then I got a position as night auditor in a reputable hotel in Los Angeles.

"One of my duties in this position was to check the cash registers in the hotel, including the bar. It was here that temptation hit me, for I couldn't get out of that bar without sneaking a few drinks. My alcoholism was now getting into high gear, and my continued binges finally resulted in my dismissal.

"My next stop was a position as dividend clerk with a stock and bond firm. It was while here that my drinking caught up with me. I became seriously ill and went to a hospital to undergo a cure. After two days there I went into delirium tremens. My stepson tried his best to have me committed to a psychopathic ward, but I convinced a sympathetic judge that while I was undoubtedly abnormal while drinking, I was thoroughly sane and competent at other times.

"I was released to go home, but shortly afterward I returned to my uncontrolled drinking. For the next three years I was too sick to work, and I spent most of my time drinking and getting over drunken escapades. My wife finally had as much as she could stand, and one day she handed me $150 on condition that I leave for Chicago immediately. She indicated that she was through.

"I started out by getting a room at a hotel to rest up for my arduous trip to Chicago, which I firmly resolved to start the next day. Of course I had to have a pint of whisky to help me relax. I kept postponing the Chicago trip from day to day, meanwhile gradually using up my slender resources for room rent and the whisky that had become such a necessary part of my life.

"Finally I became so low in mind and body, as I sat there brooding in my hotel room, that I decided to end my useless, drifting life. I wrote a note of farewell to my wife, took all the codeine pills my doctor had prescribed for my neuralgia, and lay down on my bed to await the end. As I was dozing off into what I thought was to be my last sleep, the police broke down my door—and you know the rest."

There was a long silence when Tom had finished his story. I was thinking of the thousands, yes, millions, of miserable, hopeless alcohol addicts eking out frustrated, aimless lives in the skid rows of hundreds of American cities. They are living, if you can call it that, in an alcoholic world of fantasy in which the pursuit of liquor constitutes the sole and all-important purpose of life. I thought of the broken homes, the neglected and oftentimes badly abused children, the broken marriage vows, the gradual heartbreaking physical, mental, moral, and spiritual deterioration that alcohol brings in its wake. I thought of these things, and my heart felt heavy. At last I broke the stillness that had fallen in the room. "Tell me, Tom," I asked gently, "do you honestly feel that God is the only answer to your alcoholic condition?"

I felt my arm gripped with an intensity that startled me. "Oh, doctor, I do! I do!" he cried, with such earnestness that whatever lingering doubts of his sincerity I might have had were swept instantly away. "He's my only chance, and He's also my last chance, and I know it. Oh, doctor, I'll serve God for the rest of my days to the best of my poor ability if He will only keep me from taking another drink!"

"He'll do that, Tom," I assured him; "but you must keep your eyes on Him. When you take your eyes off Him, you're in real danger of a slip. You must pray daily for wisdom to do His will and for strength and faith and courage to follow as He reveals it to you. Do you understand?"

"Yes, yes, I do!" he answered eagerly. "And I accept the terms gladly. I'm a drowning man clutching at his last chance, and I know it. I've tried everything else without success. This is the end if God fails me."

"God never fails, Tom, if we have faith and trust Him. Try it and see."

As this is written, Tom Richards's sobriety has stretched into years. He had dedicated his life to God, and he is doing outstanding work in helping other alcoholics find a way of escape.

Chapter 2

Sobriety for Women Alcoholics

SOMETHING significantly new has been added to the increasingly serious problem of alcoholism in this country today. It is the woman alcoholic. Only as recently as 1930, women alcoholics were a rarity; but when repeal came along, and with it the return of the old-time saloon in its more fashionable guise as a cocktail lounge, tavern, night club, or what have you, women drinkers came into their own. Today reliable statistics reveal that there are about six times as many men as women alcoholics; but the really significant figures are that the female rate of alcoholism rose by 33 per cent between 1940 and 1948. In the shorter and more recent period from 1945 to 1948 the female rate increased 21 per cent, while the male rate was increasing 10 per cent.

These figures represent the end product of the liquor industry—the men and women who have reached the alcoholic depths from which many are fated never to return. But, in addition to these alcoholics, there are at least as many, both men and women, who have not as yet progressed as far down the alcoholic trail of misery, degradation, and hopelessness, but who are definitely classifiable as "problem" drinkers, whose drinking is beginning to get them into trouble of various kinds.

Women alcoholics present an especially difficult treatment problem medically, sociologically, and spiritually because, traditionally and from time immemorial, the female of the species has been regarded as the guardian of the morals and the sanctity of the home. On her shoulders has fallen the major responsibility for the care of children at their most impressionable age. Her husband and her family are likely to place her on a pedestal, and the spiritual tone of the home is largely determined by her influence.

Thus, when a woman succumbs to alcoholism, there is much more at stake than merely her own personal welfare. Her children are neglected and oftentimes abused; her husband becomes little more than a meal ticket and a source of daily "handouts" to keep her supplied with the liquor she has become dependent upon. The entire structure of the home disintegrates with frightful finality, the children go untended and all too often become juvenile delinquents through association with bad company. These children often run afoul of the law and are removed from their mother's custody by court order. In other cases the husband, unable to reason with his alcoholic wife, obtains a divorce and takes the children with him. In either event the alcoholic wife makes the loss of her children an excuse for further alcoholic excesses and, before long, she reaches the inevitable skid row, where she shamelessly cadges drinks from casual male acquaintances or total strangers. By this time her morals are almost completely gone and she will unhesitantly exchange her favors for a bed, a meal, and a bottle of cheap wine.

The stigma attached to the alcoholic woman is much greater than that of her male counterpart. Society tends to overlook many of the male alcoholic's antics, but this same society will cruelly condemn a woman who does the same things when under the influence of alcohol. A man who goes on a drunken spree, gets entangled in promiscuous sex escapades, and lands in police custody can continue to live in his home neighborhood with a reasonable chance of keeping his reputation. However, a woman who finds herself in a similar position will be snubbed socially and despised because society, in spite of all its talk about the equality of the sexes, still expects women to be better behaved than men.

Personality disorders are also more likely to lead to alcoholism in women than in men. An unhappy love affair, failure in marriage, the loss of a mate, remorse over a clandestine love affair, or even the horror of growing old, are more frequently the causes of alcoholic excesses among women than among men.

In this connection the authoritative statement by George T. Harding, M.D., professor of psychiatry in Ohio State University, to the students of the Institute of Scientific Studies for the Prevention of Alcoholism, is illuminating. Says Dr. Harding: "There is always danger that the normal person who drinks moderately may turn to alcohol as an escape when faced by an abnormal situation."

Both physically and psychologically, therefore, women alcoholics have a harder row to hoe than men, partly because their entire make-up is more complex and sensitive; and, even more important, because they have been hedged in by social conventions that have brought about a myriad of inhibitions unknown to the male. Take the fairly typical history of a woman alcoholic who came to my attention in Los Angeles at our charity alcoholic clinic for women.

Rosemary Whitman was the patient, and she was the youngest daughter in an Ohio farm family living in a small town some eighty miles from Columbus. From her earliest childhood, Rosemary was an unusually beautiful girl, and, as is so often the case, she was spoiled and pampered. While her brothers and sisters had to toil at farm chores, Rosemary was kept around the farmhouse to help her mother with the less unpleasant and less arduous tasks. Her mother, a shrewd and somewhat worldly-wise woman of French Canadian extraction, was quick to realize the potential cash value of her youngest daughter's beauty if her career were properly managed. She drove away the lovesick but penniless swains who sought Rosemary's hand in marriage. She had bigger things in mind for her daughter; and when Rosemary was eighteen, mother packed her off to business college in Columbus to learn to be a secretary. She was equipped with new clothes and a liberal supply of money scrimped and saved by her designing mother for this occasion. Furthermore, Rosemary was imbued with her mother's cold and calculating nature; she had learned early in life to let her head rule her heart.

After graduation from business school the girl obtained a position with a theatrical producer in Columbus, and before long found herself being wooed ardently by a rich

New York playboy who was smitten by her unusual beauty and (he thought) naïve innocence. They were married after a whirlwind courtship, but not before Rosemary had exacted a solemn promise from him to further her dreams of a stage career.

Without too much trouble, in view of Rosemary's striking beauty, he was able to get her placed in the chorus line of Ziegfeld's Follies. Here, as a member of a world-famous show production, Rosemary enjoyed the adulation and admiration which her pleasure-loving nature demanded. Her husband granted, and even seemed to anticipate, her every wish. In due course of time she bore him two children, a boy and a girl.

Rosemary by this time had tired of the rigorous practice and rehearsal requirements of even the follies, and she decided to quit the show business and devote her time to her children and to the social activities of a rich man's wife. She became a familiar figure at the country club, the annual horse show, the charity bazaars, the Red Cross canteen, and at all the other functions attended by the recognized social leaders of Columbus. It was at this point in her life that she took her first drink. Her husband had been a heavy drinker from his youth, and he encouraged his wife in her drinking career.

Rosemary quickly developed a taste for alcohol and its aura of well-being. Without realizing it, she began to drink more than she had intended to, and her behavior began to suffer. Soon there were whispers about the "drunken Billingsleys." On the rare occasions when her husband tried to get sobered up, it was Rosemary's insistence upon having a few cocktails before dinner that started him off on another alcoholic binge. He began to drink more and more heavily, and finally he reached the stage where it was necessary for him to enter a hospital for treatment. These hospitalizations became more and more frequent with the passing years, until, after fifteen years of marriage, he died suddenly of acute alcoholism. Because of his wealth and social standing in the community, his death was ascribed to a heart attack, and only his close associates, including his wife and the family doctor, knew the real cause of his death.

Rosemary, meanwhile, had almost unconsciously increased her own drinking tempo; and when she found herself left free of the burden of her husband's alcoholism and with a half million dollars of new wealth as the result of his death, she began a career of excessive drinking. She sent the two children to private schools in New England so that she could do the things she had always wanted to do.

Poor Rosemary! Alcoholism had marked her for its victim. Within a few years after her husband's death she found herself a patient again and again in the same hospitals and sanitariums her husband had patronized. Her behavior, between such periods of involuntary sobriety, became more and more unrestrained and eccentric. It wasn't long before she had been married and divorced three or four times, with all the accompanying notoriety and scandal of the divorce courts and tabloid press. She continued to throw her inherited fortune around with reckless abandon on alcohol, parties, and worthless male companionship.

After a particularly rank court scandal the custody of

her children was taken from her and she found herself virtually penniless. She drifted slowly, inevitably, to skid row. Here she became a familiar, but by no means welcome, figure in the numerous low honky-tonks and dives that lined the squalid streets. She shamelessly begged drinks from the "winos" and other depraved and vicious characters she encountered. If it was necessary to spend the night in their company in some cheap flop-house or tawdry hotel room in order to get the liquor she craved, she found herself doing so with less and less reluctance. One morning when she awoke sick and tremulous in a sordid hotel bedroom, she found herself unaccountably shocked by the cheapness of her surround-ings and the unspeakable degradation of her life. As she lay there with hot tears of shame and remorse coursing down her cheeks, she found herself crying out to God for help.

"Oh, God," she breathed, "please, dear God, help me to lead a better life. Take away this awful craving I have for liquor and let me serve You from this day on with all my heart and soul."

An all-merciful God, looking down with infinite pity and compassion from above must have answered that heartfelt prayer. In some way Rosemary's footsteps were guided to our alcoholic clinic, and she received treatment. She was given sedation, good food, and understanding care. Gradually she emerged from the alcoholic fog, and she evinced a surprising interest in spiritual things. The manager of the clinic, Mrs. Lynch, reported her daily progress to me with growing enthusiasm.

"Rosemary has become our star patient, doctor," she

remarked one day as I was making my rounds. "She's really going all out for our spiritual program. Not only does she help out with the work around the alcoholic ward, but she is always one of the first to talk to new patients about the power of Jesus Christ. She realizes that her salvation from alcoholism depends entirely upon her reliance on God."

I had a long talk with Rosemary and was astounded at her grasp of spiritual truth. She had placed the hitherto overmastering problem of her alcoholism squarely at the Saviour's feet, and she cried out daily to Him in prayer to clean up her life. She stopped smoking and using the coarse language that had come so readily from her lips. She was a powerful and untiring worker with the other alcoholic patients; and, at Mrs. Lynch's earnest request, she was made assistant at the clinic. After leaving the clinic she has been reunited with her children and has embarked on a new life of usefulness and service for God.

But for every Rosemary who finds her way back to lasting sobriety, there are a thousand other women who sink from sight forever in the dreadful morass of alcoholism. They die a little each day as they eke out a sordid, degraded existence in cheap flophouses, greasy restaurants, and noisome bars. They find their eventual way to the potter's field and an unmarked drunkard's grave, or they die spectacularly in a leap from a hotel window or from an overdose of sleeping pills. Many of them gravitate to dope and alternate between bouts with the bottle and sessions with the needle. Such women are doomed to even swifter ruin and oblivion than is a mere alcoholic.

The only hope for lasting cure lies in the kindling of

a faith and trust in God. Alcoholics must be treated with sympathy and understanding; they must be brought to realize that the only hope for permanent recovery from their dreadful condition lies in turning their problem over to a "higher power."

They must be made to realize, perhaps even more than their male counterpart, that God means what He says when He promises to "save them to the uttermost." They must be made to grasp the fact that in God's sight no past sin, no matter how great it may appear to mortal eyes, is unforgivable when the sinner is truly repentant and turns away from his or her evildoing.

Women alcoholics are especially difficult treatment problems, largely because they are women. They try by every subterfuge and evasion possible to hide their condition from others, and by so doing they are much more likely to delude themselves as to the desperateness of their condition. It is usually harder to get a woman to admit that she is an alcoholic and in need of help for her condition than to get similar results with a man. She has a hundred plausible camouflages for her alcoholic condition, ranging from a simple cold to pneumonia, from sinus trouble to a nervous breakdown. Moreover, her husband is likely to lend a willing hand in her deception, since he feels that an alcoholic wife will ruin him in both social and business circles. When it does become known, as it will sooner or later, the woman alcoholic is hustled off to a private hospital or sanitarium to be treated for some mysterious malady she has suddenly contracted. When it is found that she is actually suffering from advanced alcoholism, her recovery is difficult.

The average woman alcoholic, while admittedly more difficult to treat medically and having a poorer chance for recovery than the man suffering from the same malady, is by no means hopeless from a spiritual viewpoint. The woman alcoholic can find peace, serenity, and total freedom from her burden if she will lay her entire problem before God and humbly and contritely ask for His help to overcome it. She must always remember that, while her recovery may seem uncertain or even hopeless to man, God is able to save even "to the uttermost."

It is especially important that the woman alcoholic be made to realize God's omnipotence and His never-failing strength. Once she recognizes the fact that she *is* an alcoholic and cries out for help to Him who never fails, her recovery is as sure and fast as is the male alcoholic's.

Chapter 3

Red Finds Sobriety

THE brief semitropical twilight had given place to the soft fragrance of a typical Hawaiian night, redolent with the heady perfume of a thousand unseen blooms. But in Honolulu's teeming, noisy Chinatown, the canopy of night merely serves to hide from view the rickety tenement buildings, the garish saloons, the clip joints, and the gambling dens that blossom like poisonous plants with the coming of darkness.

In a narrow, dusty alley that twists among the flimsy buildings, a close observer might have seen three shadowy forms huddling in the gloom. Red Burgess, a notorious Honolulu drunkard with a record of nearly a hundred arrests for intoxication, was continuing an alcoholic spree he had started some two weeks before. The others with him were chance companions he had picked up in the casual way an alcoholic will make friends after he has had a few drinks. One was a burly young man of perhaps twenty-two years, in a soldier's uniform. The other was a slenderly built Hawaiian youth, possibly in his early thirties, whose puffed, dissipated face bore unmistakable evidence of his alcoholic past.

The three men were plainly "in their cups," and had already reached the dangerous, quarrelsome stage that so often follows the initial period of exhilaration when alcohol releases the inhibitions and anesthetizes the higher functions of judgment and self-control.

"What's the idea, drinking all the bottle, Red?" the soldier demanded belligerently, as he wrathfully surveyed some four or five empty bottles littering the ground beside them. "You not only look like a pig, but you act like one!"

Red scrambled to his feet at the soldier's words. "Say, big boy, whom do you think you're talking to, anyhow? You ain't dealing with no recruit now, soldier; so pipe down before somebody gets hurt!"

"Meaning what?" the soldier demanded, also getting to his feet, but doing so slowly and deliberately and with a studied insolence that caused Red's hands to twitch.

"Aw, knock it off, you two!" The Hawaiian spoke quietly, but with a thinly veiled menace in his tone that caused the others to pause and regard him quizzically. "Quit beefing about one bottle. What's that to us, anyway?" he continued, a thin smile on his face; but his eyes were stony hard. "There's plenty more where that last one came from; and if you'll keep out of each other's hair for a few minutes, I'll make the run for another. How's that sound?"

The soldier grunted. "What's the use?" he muttered. "If this redhead gets his mitts on it first we won't be a bit better off than we are now."

Red advanced threateningly at the soldier's words. "Say, soldier, are you looking for trouble, or what is the pitch? If you don't like it here, why don't you scram?"

"That's enough of that, Red!" the slender Hawaiian interjected sharply. "What're you trying to do? Get the cops down on us like a ton of bricks? One more word out of either one of you and I'll slap you silly! If you want to try your luck right now, let's get it over with!" Red outweighed the Hawaiian by at least fifteen pounds,—the soldier by even more,—but something about the native's wiry frame and catlike movements warned him that he could be a tough opponent indeed in any rough-and-tumble encounter. With a muttered oath Red seated himself on a low stone wall that ran along one side of the alley. "Oh, all right," he mumbled; "I'll stay in my corner if that big fellow will stay in his. But one false move and I'll let him have it!"

"Oh, yeah? You and who else?" the big soldier retorted.

"Shut up, both of you!" The Hawaiian youth turned on his heel without another word and walked through the darkened alley in the direction of the nearest liquor store. Behind him he heard Red and the soldier still muttering vague threats at each other.

Fifteen minutes later the Hawaiian groped his way back, a bottle of wine under one arm. As he neared the scene of his expected rendezvous, a ray of light from a nearby house outlined the unmistakable figure of Red in a stooping position over a dark form at his feet. He was holding something clutched tightly in his right hand and was rocking backward and forward unsteadily. The Hawaiian broke into a run that brought him to Red in a few seconds. His keen glance took in the whole scene in an instant. Red had the shattered neck of a bottle in his hand. The soldier lay at his feet, inert and moaning feebly. His features were a mass of blood, and an ugly gash ran almost the entire length of his scalp.

"Well, I see you've gone ahead and done it, Red," the newcomer commented coolly. "You might as well go ahead and finish the job, because when this fellow comes to, if he ever does, he's going to do plenty of talking—and you know what that means!"

"I had to do something, Tommy!" Red replied desperately, dropping the incriminating bottle fragment and addressing the Hawaiian youth by name for the first time. "You understand that, don't you, Tommy? As soon as you left he made a pass at me; and he would have killed me, too, if I hadn't bopped him. You believe me, don't you, Tommy?" he pleaded almost tearfully, clutching at the young man's sleeve.

"Quit the sob stuff!" Tommy snarled. "You got us both in a fine fix by your bullheadedness, but there's no use crying about it now. Let's take a drink out of the bottle and then scram through the lane to Aala Park. If we're lucky, the cops will never find out who did it, and we'll be safe enough."

Unfortunately for Red and Tommy, however, the slugged man turned out to be more seriously injured than even his bloody appearance suggested. For days he hovered precariously between life and death in the Army hospital, with a compound skull fracture. Army authorities, irked beyond endurance by this latest in a long series of attacks on servicemen by local hoodlums, put pressure on Honolulu's police chief to do something about the situation. As a result, a full-scale search was made for the soldier's assailant. The liquor-store dealer, threatened with loss of his license if he didn't talk, furnished descriptions of Tommy and Red.

Both men were picked up within a matter of hours. Tommy, an ex-convict from Oahu Penitentiary, faced revocation of his parole if implicated in the affair. He naturally placed the blame squarely on Red, who was promptly arraigned in police court and then bound over to the circuit court on a charge of assault with a deadly weapon—a felony charge. His long-suffering wife put up the bond required, and Red gained his temporary freedom pending trial.

A few days later I received a visit from Mrs. Burgess at my Waikiki office. "I'm Mrs. Burgess, doctor," she began, when I had given her a seat. "I've come to have a talk with you about my husband. I've heard some good reports about the charity alcoholic clinic of which you are the medical director, and I thought perhaps you could help me. My husband's an alcoholic, but he will not admit it. He still maintains that he can take it or leave it alone, where alcohol is concerned; but if any proof were needed, this recent escapade shows that his life has become unmanageable as the result of his drinking."

I nodded. "Yes, I read in the newspapers about what happened. Is your husband still out on bond?" I asked.

A shadow fell over Mrs. Burgess' open, pleasant features. "He was until this morning, doctor; but I notified the bondsman to surrender him. In spite of all my pleas, my husband started drinking again, and you can realize it would go hard with him if he was picked up on a drunk charge with this other case still pending. So, for his own good, I told the bondsman to turn him in. He's down in the county jail now; and he's so angry he left word at the office that he doesn't want to see me. What can I do, doctor?" the wife asked desperately.

"I think you have acted wisely, Mrs. Burgess," I replied. "No one recognizes more than I do the utter futility of talking sense to a man who's been drinking. Someday your husband will thank you for what you've done. Now, in what way do you think I may be of help to your husband? I'm willing to do anything I can to assist him, because he really is in a predicament."

"If I'm not asking too much, doctor, I wonder if you could go to the jail and talk to him. You understand the alcohol problem and alcoholics better than does anyone else in town; and if anyone can get some sense into my husband's head, you can," Mrs. Burgess said earnestly.

I had to smile at the woman's deep-rooted confidence in my ability, but the pathos of her desperate clutching at a straw—any straw that might help her husband overcome his terrible habit—struck me with overpowering force.

"All I can do, Mrs. Burgess, is to try to direct his steps to God. That's the only answer for the alcoholic—complete trust and confidence that a divine power will solve a problem which seems hopeless. Tell me, is your husband a praying man?"

"No, he isn't, doctor," Mrs. Burgess replied sadly. I've tried time after time to get him to go to church with me, for I'm a member of the Lutheran Church; but he always finds some excuse for not going. I have never given up asking God's help for him, and I believe someday my prayers will be answered."

"I'll be glad to have a talk with your husband the first chance I get. The chief jailer, Mr. Kramer, is a personal friend of mine, and I know I won't have any trouble getting in. I'll make it a point to see your husband tomorrow, and I'll let you know the results of my visit."

"Oh, doctor, I knew you wouldn't fail me. I don't know how to thank you enough for what you are doing for me!" she exclaimed fervently.

We talked on for half an hour longer, and Mrs. Burgess outlined her husband's drinking career in detail. It was the familiar story of a man who had started out by drinking beer, the so-called "drink of moderation." From this seemingly innocuous start he soon felt impelled to try stronger stuff like gin and whisky. For several years he managed to steer clear of trouble. He had an occasional "Saturday-night drunk," but seldom overindulged during the week. But alcoholism is an insidious, treacherous, progressively deteriorating disease of the body and mind. Red's drinking became heavier and less easily controlled with the passing years. He began to abuse his wife with vile words and later with physical violence.

"It became impossible for me to live with him when he got on one of his drunken sprees," Mrs. Burgess said. "I'd get him a room elsewhere until he got sober enough to come back home. This usually happened after his money ran out and he became sick from drinking. Then I had to nurse him back to health again, only to have the whole heartbreaking routine repeated. I got so discouraged sometimes, doctor, I felt like throwing up my hands," she ended despondently.

"There's no doubt at all in my mind but that your husband is an alcohol addict, Mrs. Burgess. He's in a desperate plight, but no more so than the millions of other alcoholics we have throughout our nation today.*

"If your husband can somehow be brought to realize that faith in God is the only answer, he can overcome the habit that is destroying him and causing you so much unhappiness. Now, I'm going to give you two books I have found helpful in treating alcoholics. The first is called *Your Home and Health.* I want you to read it yourself before you pass it on to your husband. I know he won't see you now, but I know that after a few days in jail he'll be glad to have you call. When you go, he will be in a favorable mood to begin the spiritual education that is his only salvation. When I visit him tomorrow, I'm going to take along a copy of the second book. It is called *David Dare,* and it's another publication that has proved helpful to many alcoholic patients. Take your copy home and read it. Let me know what you think of it the next time you call. Drop in next Tuesday about ten o'clock and I think I'll have some good news for you."

Mrs. Burgess thanked me profusely and left. The next day I called on Red Burgess at Honolulu's jail. He was still resentful at having his bond surrendered; but, finally,

---

*Dr. E. M. Jellinek, formerly director of the Yale School of Alcohol Studies and now chairman of the International Committee on Alcohol Problems of the Mental Health Section of the World Health Organization, has said that there are now 3,800,000 alcoholics and 3,000,000 problem drinkers in addition, *known* to us. "But I would not argue with you," he declared in a speech given June 12, 1951, at the University of Washington, "if you said there were 7,000,000 alcoholics and problem drinkers in all the United States."

somewhat grudgingly, he admitted that his wife had prevented him from getting into deeper water by her action. After asking him if I could help him in any way, I broached the subject of drinking. I asked him if he had ever made any serious attempt to stop.

"Why, yes, I have, doctor!" he exclaimed. "I've been attending Alcoholics Anonymous meetings now for more than a year, but for some reason or other I don't seem to be able to get on the program. I know there's something that will help me; but, try as I may, it seems to be out of my grasp." He ended with a gesture of hopelessness.

"Do you mean the part about turning your problem over to God for solution?" I asked.

"Yeah, that's it, I guess," Red replied. "It's all so confusing to me. One woman got up at a meeting and said flatly that she didn't believe in God at all. In fact, when we were closing the meeting with the Lord's Prayer, she got up and walked out. At another point in that same meeting a fellow said that it wasn't really necessary to believe in God, so long as we believed in something or someone more powerful than ourselves. I got to thinking about that, and the more I thought, the more confused I became. I ended up by going on a bender, and here I am."

"Well, Red," I replied, "I'm here to help you get straightened out in your thinking. I can assure you that there is only one God and that He is the One who gave His only Son as a living sacrifice for us. Christ died on Calvary in order that our sins might be forgiven. If we put our trust in God and in Christ, all of our problems will be taken care of for us, and that includes your drinking problem. Now I am going to leave a copy of this booklet with you. It's called *David Dare*. I want you to read it through carefully and let me know what you think of it the next time I call. I'll be down to see you again soon."

Promptly at ten o'clock the next Tuesday morning Mrs. Burgess was shown into my office. There was a happy smile on her face, and it was easy to see that something had happened. I thought that it had something to do with her husband, and her first words confirmed my surmise. "Oh, doctor," she began excitedly, "the most wonderful thing has happened! Red called me up last Sunday morning and said he wanted to see me. I went down to visit him that afternoon, and all he could talk about was a book you had given him. It was that *David Dare* you said you were going to ask him to read. He told me he had read it through twice, and he wanted to know if you had any other books you could give him. He said that *David Dare* explained some things in the Bible that had been puzzling him for a long time. So I made a special trip back home and took him *Your Home and Health*. I hope you don't mind, doctor. I think it is a wonderful book. I haven't finished it myself, but what I have read has given me an entirely different idea of how to live a Christian life, and I'm hoping it will do the same for Red."

"You did exactly right, Mrs. Burgess," I said approvingly; "and your husband's new attitude certainly makes me feel hopeful that God will help effect a change in his life."

Mrs. Burgess continued to visit my office from time to time, and she reported that Red was becoming "a new man."

"I know you'll hardly believe it," she said happily on one occasion some weeks later; "but Red has quit smoking. That's something I never thought he'd do, for he's been a heavy smoker since he was a boy. And here's something that's even harder for me to fathom—he scolded me about my coffee drinking. He told me I was ruining my health. Can you imagine that? It all ended by my promising to give it up. I felt that that was a small enough sacrifice to make if it would help him overcome his alcoholism.

"There's something else I wanted to talk to you about, doctor," Mrs. Burgess continued, her voice becoming more serious. "I've received the results of some tests made by the clinic recently, and Dr. Swanson tells me that they prove conclusively that I have cancer. He gives me no longer than eighteen months to live. When he first gave me the news I was panic-stricken; but, doctor, in the past few weeks I've learned to know God as never before in my life, and I'm not afraid to die. That last book you gave me, called *Steps to Christ*, has comforted me as no other book has done except the Bible. I don't want Red to know about the doctor's verdict, so please do not say anything to him when you see him. When he comes up for trial next week I'm going to have a talk with the judge. I'll tell him about my condition and see if I can't have Red placed on probation. Then I'm going to take a trip back to Oregon to see my folks for the last time. Doctor, would you have a few words of prayer with me to thank God for His goodness?"

As I knelt with this good woman, whose first thoughts even in her own tragic predicament were for her husband, my heart overflowed with pity and compassion. In spite of my strongest efforts, my voice shook with emotion as I said a few words of thanksgiving to the Guardian of our lives.

Red was given probation as his wife had asked, and a few days later they left for Oregon. During the next few months I received letters from both of them—letters that clearly reflected their continuing spiritual growth. About two months after their departure from Honolulu, Red wrote me that he was taking a Bible correspondence course he had heard advertised on the air.

"Do you know," he wrote, "I never dreamed that a study of the Bible could be so fascinating and helpful. Wilma and I are studying it together at nights, and we can hardly wait for the mailman to bring the next lesson."

Some weeks later I received bad news myself. A message arrived from Los Angeles stating that my father, who was also a physician, had suffered a stroke and was in serious condition. I packed my clothes and caught the first plane out of Honolulu.

When I arrived at his bedside, it was evident that my father's days of active medical practice were numbered. I talked things over with my mother, and we decided that it would be best for me to give up my Honolulu practice and move to Los Angeles to be near dad, and also to keep his practice going while he convalesced.

After I had been in Los Angeles about two months, I received word from Red that Wilma had died suddenly in her sleep. From the heartbroken tone of Red's letter I knew that he was hard hit, and, knowing his alcoholic background, I feared for the worst. I am glad to say that I had underestimated the comforting power of God in Red's case. Instead of turning to the bottle, as he most certainly would have done a few months before, Red turned to God for consolation in the hour of bereavement. The weeks and months of Bible study had built a sturdy bulwark against all the crises of life, and he weathered the storm of his grief without falling back on alcohol.

About a month later he called at my office. I hardly knew him. He was clear-eyed, brisk, and confident. When his wife's name was mentioned, he told me simply: "Doctor, I know that Wilma and I will meet again someday. We both gave our hearts to God before she died, and we tried our best to do His will. I've put my old life of drinking, gambling, smoking, and sin behind me forever. Day by day I'm trying to do God's will better, and I'm striving to please Him."

It's been almost four years now since Red had his last drink of alcohol. He is continuing to grow spiritually, and he spends a good portion of his spare time in aiding other alcoholics to attain sobriety through faith and trust in the infallible power of God. From all reports, he is now engaged in an all-out effort to bring the truth about the curse of so-called social drinking to the youth of his community.

Here was another life, once almost hopelessly enmeshed in evil, saved by the One who never fails when we turn our lives over to His guidance and keeping.

Chapter 4

Meet Harry and Georgia

Harry Lundigan's neighbors, business associates, and about everyone else that he came in contact with were agreed that he had the "Midas touch"—the rare ability to make money where others could barely eke out an existence or would fail entirely. Furthermore, his friends all agreed that Harry could almost "charm the birds out of the trees." Broad-shouldered, six feet two, with dark, curly hair and mischievous blue Irish eyes, he was irresistible to women and admired by men for his masculinity. One businessman said in awe-stricken tones: "That fellow Lundigan could sell a football to a one-legged man!"

The outlook was promising for Harry Lundigan when he graduated from the University of Southern California's School of Business Administration. As an outstanding athlete and campus hero during his college days, the name Lundigan was magic. Now he was besieged with offers of employment. Brokerage houses, banks, oil companies, insurance firms, and advertising agencies vied with one another for his handsome face. Harry cast an appraising eye over these bids and decided that his future

lay in the advertising field. He became a junior executive with a well-known Los Angeles agency, and his rise
was meteoric. Within a year he had become production
manager, in two years he was vice-president, and the
following year he took the president's chair.

Under his direction the agency flourished as it never
had before, even in its palmiest days. Advertising accounts that had previously resisted the strongest bland-
ishments of Harry's predecessor fell like rich plums into
his lap. But, like Alexander of old, Harry soon sighed for
new worlds to conquer. Why should he work for someone else, he thought, when he could be putting these
lush profits into his own pocket? When Harry put his
idea into action by purchasing a small advertising agency
that was about to fail, his friends were aghast. What
madness was this? Had Harry's early flamboyant suc-
cesses warped his judgment?

It didn't take long for the head-wagging doubters to
find out what was in the wind. Within a matter of hours
the agency's creditors were sent on their way paid in full,
and the sign painters had neatly inscribed the legend
"Harry Lundigan Advertising Agency" on the door. The
new venture was officially under way. It was almost fan-
tastically successful from the start, and it set a pattern
that was to continue through the next ten years as Harry
added new and glittering links to an advertising chain
that eventually spanned the continent.

In the meantime the "boy genius" who had set the
advertising world afire took time out to fall in love.
Harry seemed to be as lucky in love as he had been in
business. Certainly the girl of his choice appeared to

have every attribute any man would want. Petite, dark-eyed, and vivacious, Georgia Blackwood possessed almost as much personal magnetism in a feminine way as did her noted husband as a representative of the male sex. But over and above these purely physical attributes, Georgia possessed a glowing spirituality that set her apart. She had been reared in a Christian home. Tobacco and alcohol were abhorrent to her, especially the latter, and she had never tasted either tea or coffee. Her ethical values were on the highest possible plane, and it was probably because she did represent the best in Christian womanhood that she exerted such a strong appeal to Harry Lundigan. On her part, and like so many others who met him, she felt herself almost irresistibly drawn to Harry right from their first meeting, even though she realized that there were habits in his life of which she could not approve. It was at this point that she made the fatal mistake that blinds so many women in love. She thought that after marriage she could change Harry's ways. How much unhappiness, heartache, and misery she could have avoided but for her belief in that popular fallacy!

Some say that love is blind, and there was no doubt that Georgia had "fallen hard." Apparently Harry was equally smitten. He sensed Georgia's unspoken disapproval of his smoking and so-called social drinking. Fearful of losing her, he promised faithfully to quit both pernicious habits—and for several years after their marriage he kept his promise. But business and social contacts continued to press in upon him as his advertising empire spread, and, furtively at first at later openly, he resumed both of his former habits. Georgia pretended to overlook Harry's backsliding, but her heart was heavy as she watched his moral fiber disintegrate, and his open, carefree disposition turn morose and moody.

Two daughters had been born to Harry and Georgia, and, although outwardly Harry lavished his affection on them, it was evident to Georgia's discerning nature that Harry had been bitterly disappointed at not having a son to step into his shoes someday.

Almost imperceptibly Harry's drinking got heavier, and as surely his indifference to Georgia and the children increased. On a sunny spring morning the Lundigans were breakfasting together in the beautifully appointed dining room of their luxurious Beverly Hills home. The two girls, Sandra, twelve, and Joan, nine, were whispering together about some secret, while Georgia busied herself with the serving of the meal. The master of the house had a newspaper shielding his face; he was moodily staring at the stock-market reports. His head throbbed from his alcoholic overindulgence of the night before, and he was in a surly, uncommunicative mood.

"Harry," said Georgia, pausing in her task of pouring two glasses of milk. No response.

"Oh, Harry!" This time in a slightly louder tone. The newspaper rustled ominously. Finally it lowered completely to reveal a pair of bloodshot eyes, an unshaven, slightly puffed face, and a baleful glare.

"What now?" he rasped. "Can't you see I'm busy reading? If there's anything you need for yourself or the girls, go ahead and get it! Don't bother me. I'm not feeling at all well this morning."

4—E.A.

Georgia found herself suddenly close to tears. This was the man she married, the man she once thought she loved to the exclusion of all others—the carefree, good-natured, considerate Harry Lundigan. Could this morose, sullen man be the same person? It didn't seem possible. She looked at him with eyes that filled with hot tears despite her best efforts to hold them back.

"Well, what is it?" Harry rasped again with ill-concealed impatience, as the two girls instinctively felt the tension mount between their parents.

Georgia began bravely but hesitantly as she noted Harry's darkening looks. "Well, you remember, last week you said you'd go with Sandra and Joan and me to church services today and — "

"Aw, I must have been nuts when I promised that," Harry cut in brutally. "You know what I think about religion. It's all right for weak sisters and old women, but it's not for me. I'll make out all right without it, thank you. I have so far, and I see no reason to think things are going to change; do you? You run along with the kids while I catch up a little on my sleep. That conference with Richardson last night left me a wreck, but I need a loan from the old fellow and I have to at least pretend he doesn't make me sick every time I look at him."

He managed a sickly smile and his voice softened slightly. "You do understand, don't you, Georgia? I'm in no condition to make it this morning; but you take the girls along, and I'll see you later. We'll take a drive this afternoon in Griffith Park Would you like that, kids?" he asked suddenly, addressing the two silent girls.

"But, daddy, you promised mommy that you'd go to church with us today. Why don't you come with us, daddy?" Joan entreated, her delicately rounded face, so like Georgia's with its luminous brown eyes, turned appealingly to her father's.

"Next week for sure, Joannie," Harry said, a trace of his old affectionate nature showing for an instant. "Daddy's not feeling well this morning; but this afternoon I'll take you both for a ride on the ponies at Griffith Park. Would you like that?"

Little Joan clapped her hands gleefully. "Oh, daddy, will you really? That'll be super!" Sandra's face lighted up, too, at the mention of ponies; but as she glanced at her mother's face, she suddenly shared the grief she saw there, without completely understanding why.

"Harry, I hardly think this is the day to do that," Georgia said quietly.

Harry's face lost whatever slight trace of geniality it might have had. "And why not, if I may be so rude as to ask?" he said in an ugly tone. "I suppose you won't go to heaven if you do—is that it?" he demanded, his voice rising ominously.

Georgia faced him bravely. "Need I remind you I have always made it a practice to put aside one day in the week to reverence God," she said quietly. "When we were married you agreed that neither one of us would interfere with the other's religious beliefs. In fact, if you will recall, you promised to join my church; but of course I'm not going to try to make you do anything you don't want to do in your heart," she ended sadly, a faraway look in her eyes.

"You'd better not try," Harry flared suddenly. "Believe me, you'd better not. Georgia, let's get all this ridiculous religious tomfoolery settled once and for all time. I don't care if you go to church. I don't even care if you want to become a Buddhist or a Mohammedan. But let's be sensible about it. I say the girls are going to go to Griffith Park and ride the ponies this afternoon, and that's that. I don't want to hear anything more about it!" he concluded, thrusting his chin forward belligerently toward Georgia.

Joan unexpectedly started to cry, and Sandra hurried her out of the room, near tears herself. A tense silence fell between Harry and Georgia.

"I'm getting tired of this continual yak-yakking about religion, Georgia," Harry continued when the girls had gone. What're you trying to do, anyway—make nuns out of the two girls? They're normal American girls—or were before you started trying to make plaster saints out of them. I'm going to see to it that they have all the fun that's coming to them. From now on, kindly leave me out of anything that is even remotely connected with church. I don't even want any mention of it made while I'm around. If you want to believe it, that's your business; but leave me out of it; understand?" Harry's voice had unconsciously become louder as his temper rose, and when he ended he was almost shrieking.

"It isn't necessary to shout at me like that, Harry," Georgia said quietly. "I think we understand each other perfectly. But I insist upon one thing, and that is the right to bring our children up in the Christian faith. I'm going to see to it that they attend Sabbath school and church at least once a week, but I suppose you will have your own way with them in between times."

Harry suddenly changed his attitude. "Now you're being halfway sensible, Georgia," he said. "There's no reason why we should let some ridiculously silly thing come between us. After all, Georgia, I still have an awfully soft spot in my heart for you; you know that, don't you?" He tried to put his arm around his wife's waist, but succeeded in only a clumsy gesture. Georgia instinctively drew away from him. Her eyes filled with tears and she looked sadly at her husband.

"Oh, Harry," she sobbed, "you don't realize what you are saying. This isn't a 'ridiculously silly thing;' it's something that will decide where you are going to spend eternity. Can't you see that, Harry?"

"No, frankly, I can't, Georgia, and, please, let's not go over that again. When Harry Lundigan wanes and turns up his toes, well, that's all there is, as far as I'm concerned. So let's forget about it, Georgia. I'm going upstairs and get a little shut-eye."

Harry pecked a kiss at Georgia's unresponsive face and then disappeared through the door on the way to his bedroom. Georgia turned sadly back to the breakfast table and started picking up the dishes. It was the maid's day off, and Georgia stacked the dishes in the kitchen before readying herself and the children for the church services.

The Lundigan home had changed in the thirteen years after a marriage that was entered into with hope and with the mutual pledging of respect and love. Like a gnawing, corrosive poison, alcohol had done its insidious work. Alcoholism is a progressively deteriorating disease which attacks man's highest functions first. It kills all that is finest, and then weakens its victims by depriving them even of their physical functions. Last of all, of course, it may take away life itself.

Chapter 5

Harry's Fatal Decision

HARRY Lundigan, once embarked on the slippery downhill slide, began to find the going rough indeed. His mind, clouded by the daily doses of alcohol that had by now become a necessity of life, betrayed him on several occasions, and this resulted in faulty judgment that cost him thousands of dollars. The word soon got around that Harry was "hitting the bottle," and his business competitors were quick to take advantage of his lapses. Within a few years he became a near physical wreck, and his business dwindled to the point where foreclosure by his creditors seemed imminent.

Harry became a familiar figure in the various hospitals and sanitariums in and around Los Angeles as he attempted to get over his alcoholism. He even managed to get himself arrested two or three times as he staggered about town. "Lundigan's on the way out," said the same men and women who had fawned over him only a few years before.

Meanwhile Georgia watched Harry's growing degradation with helpless despair. Life became a nightmare of broken promises, threats, and even physical violence.

Then, almost as hard to bear, were intervals of remorse and tearful self-accusation, followed invariably by even more violent and prolonged drinking bouts. Finally Georgia was obliged to lock herself and the two girls in their room whenever her husband went on one of his sprees—which became almost unbroken. One day things reached a climax when Harry returned half drunk and belligerent as Georgia and the two girls were having dinner. He was disheveled, unshaven, and in an especially ugly mood.

"Well, I must say you might at least have waited for me before starting to eat," he greeted his family. "Or don't I count around here any more—eh, is that it?" His bloodshot eyes glared balefully at the silent group at the table. "Getting to be too good to associate with me, eh?" he continued, gradually working himself up into a fury. "Well, I'll show you who's running this joint, you can bet you life on that!"

The two girls, their eyes wide with fear, started to leave the table. "Sit down, you two!" Harry roared. "What's the idea of trying to sneak away? Are you scared of your old man, or what is the score?" The two girls stopped halfway out of their chairs and looked appealingly at their mother. Harry noticed the direction of their glances and his fury mounted.

"Never mind what she says," he shouted. Then, pounding his fist heavily on the table, he added, "I'm the boss of this house and what I say goes." His voice had risen until it was almost a shriek. "That means you, too, you sniveling, sanctimonious church lover." He was venting his fury on Georgia. The wife remained silent, knowing all too well from other scenes that any reply would serve only to further inflame the passions of this creature she could no longer look upon as her husband without experiencing a shudder of revulsion.

"All right, don't sit there like a dummy. Say something, will you?" Harry jeered, thrusting his face within a few inches of Georgia's. The woman continued silent, but she was pale. Suddenly Harry drew his hand back and struck Georgia brutally across the face. The unexpectedness of the blow caused her to lose her balance, and she fell to the floor. The two girls suddenly came to life and rushed to the prostrate form of the mother as Harry, like a man coming out of a dream, swayed against the table, rubbing his eyes and mumbling to himself.

"Oh, mommy, mommy," cried Sandra, dropping to her knees beside Georgia and trying to raise her from the floor, with Joan's aid. "Daddy's hurt you, and I hate him! I hate him! I hate him!" She spat out the last with an intensity that would have astounded anyone unacquainted with the facts.

"Oh, what have I done? What have I done?" Harry moaned in a tone suddenly maudlin with a drunkard's self-pity." I'm sorry, Georgia, really and truly I am!" He lurched toward her and attempted to help her to her feet.

"Get away from her, you—you beast!" Sandra shouted, the fear of her father overcome by her concern for her mother. "You've done enough harm already. Why don't you leave her alone and go back to that saloon you like so much?" Harry, startled by the vehemence of his daughter's attack, retreated a step from her onslaught.

"Yes, please leave me alone, Harry," said Georgia,

speaking for the first time since Harry entered the room. She got up slowly from the floor, a livid mark on her cheek still visible from the blow she had received. "Either you are going to have to move out or the two girls and I are going to mother's. I can't stand any more of this; that's all there is to it!"

"Don't leave me, Georgia! Don't leave me!" Harry entreated, sinking to his knees. "I need you. I haven't a single friend in the world I can talk to except you! I'll be good, I swear I will. I'll never take another drink again as long as I live; but don't leave me—oh, please don't leave me!" Covering his face in his arms, Harry gave way to uncontrollable sobbing.

Georgia regarded him silently, a look of mingled pity and scorn on her face. It was an old, familiar scene to Georgia and the two girls by now, and they knew the inherent insincerity and evanescence of it all. All too many times had they seen him get drunk again within a few hours after making similar promises.

"There's only one condition on which I'll promise to remain," Georgia said finally. "You must turn yourself in as a patient to an alcoholic clinic I heard about recently. That's final!"

"Georgia, you know I haven't the money to pay for any kind of treatment. If I had, there's nothing I'd like better than to get straightened around and back on the job; you know that!"

"I didn't say anything about money," Georgia replied coldly. "I'll take care of the financial end; but I want to make it clear that this is your last chance. What's your decision? Will you enter the clinic?"

"Yes, I'll go," Harry replied; "but first I'll have to have an eye opener. I'll be back in a few minutes, and then we'll go to this clinic. Where is it, by the way?" he asked.

"It's downtown," Georgia replied evasively. "There won't be any eye openers, however, or the whole deal is off. I'm not going to be embarrassed any further by having to take you in drunk to another hospital. That last experience at the general hospital is still fresh in my mind. Now, go upstairs and shave, take a bath, and put on some clean clothes. I'll be ready and waiting for you when you come down."

Harry started to protest, but, seeing the look of determination on Georgia's face, he thought better of it. He turned without another word and stumbled up the stairs.

"Oh, mommy, why don't you tell him to go away and leave us alone?" Sandra asked. "I get so mad when he abuses you that someday I'm going to fight back."

"You mustn't talk that way, Sandra," Georgia reproved her daughter quietly. "God loves us all, including your daddy. He's a sick person, and he doesn't realize what he's doing much of the time. The Bible tells us that we must forgive those who use us despitefully; and you must always remember that, no matter what he does, he's still your father. He has a soul that is dear to God, and if there is any way that I can help bring him to his senses, I'm going to do it. We are told that we should never give up trying to help a victim of drink, and I'll never stop trying to help your father."

"Mommy, you're wonderful," exclaimed Sandra, her eyes shining with love. "You have the love of Jesus in

your heart. Will this clinic really help daddy? He's tried
so many of them, and still he keeps on drinking."

"This one is different from the others, as far as I can
gather," Georgia replied. "It not only gets men sobered
up, but it also teaches them that their only hope of staying that way is to trust completely in God's power. The
doctor in charge is a Christian who brings not only
medical, but spiritual, help to his patients."

"Oh, mommy, do you think he can do the same for
daddy?" Sandra exclaimed, her face alight with hope.
"You know, sometimes when daddy's sober, he's almost
as he used to be when I was a little girl—so kind and
thoughtful and everything. How I wish they would
close up all those saloons and liquor stores where they
sell the stuff that makes daddy act the way he does! We'll
keep on praying for him; won't we, mommy? Perhaps
God will answer our prayers and make daddy as he used
to be."

"Yes, Sandra; we'll never stop praying for your father,"
Georgia answered sadly.

Harry Lundigan entered the charity alcoholic clinic on
Los Angeles's skid row while still under the influence of
alcohol. When its effect had worn off, he was a pitiful
sight,—sick, tremulous, and incoherent,—a borderline
delirium tremens case. It was at this juncture that he first
came to my attention.

I immediately realized the futility of talking to him
about his problem until his mind had been given an opportunity to clear up. I merely administered enough
sedation to give him a good night's rest, and, after checking the other patients, I left him and made some house

calls on my regular medical practice. The following morning I saw Harry again. Although the immediate danger of his having delirium tremens seemed to have been averted, he was still in a highly nervous condition.

"Harry," I began, "I suppose you realize that you are a very sick man. There's no use to pretend otherwise, and I don't see how any useful purpose can be attained by attempting to hide the truth from you. How long have you been on this particular drinking bout?"

"About six months, doctor," he mumbled. "I've been drinking every day for the past five or six years."

"What do you drink mostly—whisky?" I asked.

"Yes, I usually start on that, doctor, but when my money runs out, I drink wine, beer, or almost anything else I can get my hands on. I've even drunk hair tonic and bay rum when I needed a drink bad enough."

I could see that Harry had hit bottom in his drinking. He was in the same category as the 45,000 or more alcoholic derelicts who roam Los Angeles's skid row east of Main Street day and night in search of cheap wine to blot out their almost insupportable misery.

I talked with Harry again a few days later when the alcoholic cobwebs had blown away, at least partially. "Now, Harry," I began, "I'm not going to try to preach to you, because I know that's been done many times before without any success. I am going to tell you right now that unless you change your way of life you are going to wind up in either an insane asylum or a cemetery —and that, probably before you realize." Little did I think, as I spoke, how true my prediction would prove to be.

"Is it really that bad, doctor?" he asked. "You know, I've found that you doctors are always trying to throw a scare into us fellows who take a few drinks. I don't scare easily, and besides I know it's only a matter of will power. That's all a guy really needs to stop drinking. I haven't been using mine, that's the trouble. But, believe me, it's going to be different this time! I'll show them that Harry Lundigan may be down, but that he's far from out."

"That, Harry, is precisely the type of thinking that is keeping you and thousands of other alcoholics like you here from ever getting well. How much longer will you butt your head against a wall before you begin to realize your utter inability to pull yourself out of the alcoholic mess you're in?" I asked.

"No, Harry, you can't do it by yourself," I continued. "But if you get down on your knees and cry out to God for help, you'll get it. I know you will, because God promises to hear our prayers. I can show you dozens of men today who have achieved permanent sobriety and happiness simply because they have turned their drinking problem over to One who never fails."

"Here we go again," Harry sighed. "I knew we'd get around to religion sooner or later. Listen, doctor, I appreciate your help and all that; but let's leave religion out of this, please! It's all right, I suppose, for some guy who hasn't enough backbone to face life; but it's definitely no go with me! I can straighten myself out on my own hook; and what's more, I'll prove it to you within a week or two."

"Harry," I replied, a little irked by the contemptuous

tone he was using, "your record, if it proves anything at all, shows conclusively your incapability to control your drinking—much less stop it. Now, if you sincerely want a permanent basis for sobriety, here are the things you'll have to do. It's a tough schedule, I'll admit, and no one is expected to make it 100 per cent; but if you'll follow this program to the best of your ability and put your trust in the Lord and ask Him for renewed strength each day, you'll never want to take another drink as long as you live! Here's what you'll have to do:

"First, you will have to face the fact that you can never hope to do anything constructive and lasting about your alcoholism through your efforts alone.

"Second, you must put your complete faith and trust in God as your only means of salvation from the terrible habit that is destroying you.

"Third, you must make up your mind to turn your entire life and all its problems over to God, without mental reservations of any kind.

"Fourth, you must confess your sins to God, withholding nothing.

"Fifth, you must examine your heart and, no matter how much it may hurt you, face up squarely and without flinching to what you find there.

"Sixth, you must humbly pray for God's forgiveness, not only for your alcoholism, but for everything else in your life that you know displeases Him.

"Seventh, in so far as it is possible, you must remedy the wrongs you have done to others during your past life, praying for a knowledge of God's will and the power to do it.

"Eighth, you must make a habit of daily prayer, asking God for guidance to do His will, not yours.

"Ninth, you must be prepared, in the moments of temptation that come to you from time to time, to seek God for help.

"Tenth, having acknowledged God as your Helper, you must continue to grow spiritually from day to day through the study of the Bible and by prayer.

"Eleventh, you must make a continuing study of the principles of healthful living, putting aside those things that interfere with the development of a healthy body and a sound mind.

"Twelfth, having received God's help in your own life, you must share the rich blessing conferred upon you with those who are still in spiritual darkness.

"Thirteenth, you must seek in every way possible to enlighten others, particularly youth who have never tasted alcoholic beverages, as to the pitfalls inherent in alcohol. You must do your utmost to combat the liquor traffic through educational means and by your own personal example.

"Fourteenth, if you truly believe that Jesus died for your sins on the cross of Calvary, all other steps will come easily. Daily study of the life of Christ in the New Testament, especially the closing scenes, accompanied by heartfelt prayer for increase of faith in Jesus and His atoning sacrifice for you, will miraculously make you an overcomer and a victorious Christian.

"I might say, Harry, that there's nothing new about the program I have outlined. It's based on Christ's teachings, and it can be found in your Bible. It's the basis on which first the Washingtonians and more recently the Alcoholics Anonymous organization have founded their programs. What do you think of that, Harry?"

The man had been listening with a half-amused, bored look on his face as I talked to him. When I had finished, he said:

"It all sounds nice and plausible, doctor; but, as I said before, it's strictly no good as far as I'm concerned. Now, I'm in pretty good shape today, and in a couple of days more I'll be as fit as a fiddle again. I have a big deal cooking up with some businessmen downtown that'll put me right back where I used to be—on top of the pile. They've agreed to finance me in another advertising agency, and you know yourself those boys wouldn't be putting up their cold cash if they didn't think I was going to put the thing over."

I had been listening to him with growing consternation, for I had heard the same self-boastful words a hundred times before from other lips. "Harry, if you leave here before you have had a chance to get on a spiritual program, you are heading for disaster. Now, take my advice and give God a chance to change your life. You'll never regret it, believe me!"

"It's no go, doctor," he replied. "I can't stomach that wishy-washy religious stuff. But I thank you for what you have done for me, and someday I'll prove to you that I can and will do it alone."

Two days later Harry Lundigan left the alcoholic clinic, and in the pressure of my medical duties I forgot him temporarily. But one morning about three weeks later I opened my newspaper and saw the headlines:

"Drunken Father Kills Wife and Self After Slashing Daughter With Knife."

I almost skipped the story because such sordid accounts have become almost commonplace in a society that tolerates the unrestricted and unregulated sale of liquor. But, as I started to turn the page, my eye caught a familiar name in the first paragraph.

"Harry Lundigan," the story began, "former noted advertising executive, and his wife, Georgia, are dead today, and the couple's daughter Sandra is in a critical condition in the general hospital as the aftermath of what police described as a drunken attack by Lundigan in their home."

The story went on to say that Harry had been on a prolonged drinking spree, and when he was told by his wife that she was leaving him and taking their two daughters with her, he had grabbed a kitchen knife and stabbed Georgia to death. Sandra had attempted to wrest the knife away from her drink-maddened father and had been badly slashed in the process. Harry had then turned the full force of his fury on Sandra and tried to stab her, too; but she had eluded him and fled to a neighbor's home for help. When the police arrived on the scene shortly afterward, both Georgia and Harry lay dead. For some totally unknown reason, possibly because he had temporarily forgotten her existence in his drunken state, Harry had made no attempt to harm Joan, who was asleep upstairs unaware of the tragedy.

I sat and mused for a few moments after reading the article. Here was the stark tragedy that alcohol had brought upon an innocent Christian woman of high ideals. Through absolutely no fault of her own, and in spite of all her efforts to help her husband, she had been the victim of a drunken attack. As I thought of Harry's brilliant but blighted life, it wasn't hard for me to put my finger squarely on the cause of his failure to recover from his alcoholism. It was that he had consistently refused to allow God to come into his life, when to do so would have ended his alcoholic troubles.

If only more people would realize that psychiatry, medicine, hospitals, sanitariums, this cure and that cure, are all virtually powerless unless they are accompanied by the saving grace of God! If only people could be made to see that there is an escape, not in a drugstore, hospital, or any other institution made by man, but in heaven's power.

The only way of escape for the alcoholic is through our Saviour, Jesus Christ, who died to save men from their alcoholism as well as from all other sins. May we remember that when we attempt to treat the drinker.

Chapter 6

Death in a Bottle

WITH a salvo of shrieks the shrill cacophony of mingled police and fire sirens shattered the early morning quiet of downtown Los Angeles. Mounting higher and ever higher as the police cars and fire trucks thundered through the city's skid row to their rendezvous at Third Street, below Main, the sirens were joined by new, equally shrill and insistent voices until the chorus became almost deafening.

As the trucks clattered past the shuttered saloons, pawn shops, and rickety flophouses that dot the street like festering sores, many a befuddled wino stirred uneasily on his filthy cot.

"Hey, Mac; there must be a big fire somewhere," one mumbled to another in their room. "It sounds like every fire wagon in town's on its way!"

"Aw, be quiet, will you?" his companion said irately. "Go back to sleep. What do you care if the whole town burns down? You don't own any apartment buildings."

The big ladder truck screeched to a halt in front of a six-story building bearing the name St. George Hotel. Leaping agilely to the ground, the firemen immediately started to raise the extension ladder toward the windows where several white, panic-stricken faces could be seen.

"Looks as if it has a big start, Bill," remarked the driver to a burly fellow fireman who was swiftly cranking the ladder upward.

"It looks as though someone was asleep at the switch. The alarm should have been turned in twenty minutes ago, from the looks of things," the fireman answered.

"Hey, you! Don't jump!" the fireman at the ladder suddenly bellowed to a man who had clambered out on a window ledge on the top floor and was now poised uncertainly. "We'll have this ladder up there in a jiffy to get you."

Smoke was billowing out of the windows, and an occasional streak of orange flame licked out like an adder's tongue, telling only too clearly that the fire within was raging with growing intensity. The frantic calls for help swelled in volume as half-clad, terrified men and women begged and pleaded for help.

"Don't jump, lady! We're on our way up. Take it easy. All right, Mac, we'll get you in a second, as soon as we take care of that lady in the room above you. Hey, you up there, get off that ledge—don't you—!"

There was a piercing shriek from high above the side-walk, and a white-clad figure plummeted to the alley alongside the hotel. There was a sickening crunch of flesh and bone as the man's body struck the unyielding surface. He lay sprawling and inert in a grotesque posture of sudden, violent death.

The burly fireman muttered an oath beneath his breath. "The fool; we would have had him in a couple of seconds more. He's likely to panic those other folks!" He roared suddenly, his voice rising above the crackle of flames, "Keep cool up there, we're on our way!"

A fire captain elbowed his way to the edge of the milling crowd. "Hey, Phillips," he said, addressing one of the sweating firemen; "get Walsh, Cameron, Ritchie, and Porter, and go through that sixth floor. That's where most of the smoke is, although the fire seems to have started on the third floor. Take a couple of stretchers with you and also an inhalator. There might still be someone trapped in a room up there. Check all the rooms and then report to me. Is that clear?"

"Yes, sir; we'll get going right away, captain!" replied Phillips, hastening to round up his fellow fire fighters.

A few minutes later, equipped with gas masks and carrying two stretchers and an inhalator, the five firemen groped their way through the swirling, choking fumes.

"Looks as though everyone made it out of here O.K.," remarked one of the searching party. "I guess they got— hey, what's this?" His voice rose sharply as he opened the door to room 632 and made out four shadowy, indistinct forms lying in ominous stillness.

"There's four of 'em in here, fellows. Lend a hand, will you?" he shouted as his companions quickly followed him into the smoke-filled room.

A half-filled gallon jug of wine and several empty quart bottles told the tragic story. The four men had obviously celebrated the evening before. The cheap, poisonous ersatz "wine" they had consumed had benumbed them like an anesthetic. Thus when the first telltale wisps of smoke started to seep into their room from below, they stirred uneasily, coughed once or twice as the acrid fumes reached their nostrils and then seared their lungs; but they were unable to shake off the overpowering lethargy and mental fogginess the drink had caused. One of the men, evidently by supreme effort, had crawled halfway to the doorway and lay outstretched as though begging for mercy. The other three were still lying on their disheveled beds, their faces distorted in hideous grimaces of pain and fear. In the brief flash of semiconsciousness they had before the smoke engulfed them with dreadful finality, they had found eternity upon them.

"This one here's still breathing, lieutenant!" one of the firemen shouted as he bent over the man lying nearest the door. "Give me a hand with a stretcher, fellows, and we'll take him down to the lobby and see if we can't bring him round. The rest look as if they're goners."

"Take this redheaded fellow down first," the lieutenant commanded crisply; "then come back and take the others."

A few minutes later the four men were stretched out on the floor of the hotel lobby, while trained resuscitation squads worked over them. For a while it seemed as if the slender, redheaded man was going to live, but then his face turned a mottled purple and the faint movement of his chest stopped abruptly.

"He's gone, too," remarked a shirt-sleeved, gray-haired man as he applied a stethoscope to the dead man's chest. "Move him over with the other three, will you?" he continued. "There's nothing more we can do for any of these guys, but there are lots of others needing attention."

Thus died Red Simpson, Blackie Smith, Slim Wilson,

and Fatso Greer—done to death as surely and irrevocably as though they had been shot or stabbed by an unseen assassin. For no poison concocted by the murderous Borgias could have done its work more completely or with more dreadful finality than did the lethal beverage, wine, that they had consumed the evening before.

The news of the deaths of the four men reached me at about nine o'clock that morning as I was making my rounds at the alcoholic clinic. All four men had, at one time or another, been alcoholic patients in the clinic. All of them were skilled workmen of one kind or another; but the dreadful blighting influence of alcohol had taken its toll and rendered them unfit for work except during rare intervals of sobriety.

"Are you sure of your facts?" I asked my wide-eyed informant. "I was talking to three of those fellows only last night. Is it not possible there is some mistake?"

"None at all, doctor," replied the man. "The coroner's office called and gave us their names. They want some information regarding relatives."

I had indeed seen three of the men the night before. Blackie, Slim, and Fatso had accosted me as I left the clinic about ten o'clock on my way to make some house calls.

"Hey, there, doctor!" Blackie had greeted me. "How's chances for getting two bits for something to eat?"

Blackie was so drunk that he was leaning against a nearby wall to keep from falling down. A little further up the street I saw Slim Wilson teetering around, trying to maintain his equilibrium while he asked passers-by for enough money to buy another jug of wine. A few steps from him, Fatso Greer was engaged in a heated debate with another ragged, unshaven derelict only slightly less drunk than himself.

"What's the idea, drinking out of my bottle, ya bum?" he was shouting indignantly, while he waved a finger under the other man's nose. "What you think this is, anyhow—a free wino canteen? I got a good mind to punch you in the nose, you chiseling tramp! Why, for two—" He broke off suddenly as he spotted me.

"Well, if it ain't my old friend, Dr. Hewitt!" he exclaimed, peering myopically in my direction, his quarrel over the wine temporarily forgotten. "Say, doctor!" he continued, sinking his voice to a hoarse whisper, "you wouldn't have a dime that ain't working, would you? We're just a dime short on a jug, and then we're all going over to Red's room at the St. George to flop for the night. How's about it, doctor?" he pleaded.

"Well, at least you're frank about what you want it for," I remarked dryly. "Listen to me, Fatso; you're all so drunk now that no liquor store will sell you any more."

"Are you kidding, doctor? Say, as long as you have a dime and can crawl into the store, those jokers'll give you a jug—don't worry about that! I got to get Blackie and Slim off the street before the law snatches them."

"You're not so sober yourself, Fatso, and if you'll take my advice you won't have anything more to drink tonight. Have something to eat and then go over and go to sleep. You're all as drunk now as you can get, and another drink will put you to sleep, that's all. Where's Red?" I asked, suddenly noting the absence of the other member of the foursome.

"Aw, he's passed out over at the St. George," Fatso answered disgustedly. "I couldn't even get him on his feet to do a little panhandling. But Red has a pretty good head when he's got it, and, besides, we figger on flopping in his room, so I guess we had better take him a drink or we'll sure hear about it!"

It would seem incredible to the average person that any liquor-store proprietor, avaricious and remorseless as his kind are, would have the nerve to serve these drunken men more poison with which to stupefy themselves. Most persons do not fully perceive the utterly self-centered, irresponsible attitude of the liquor dealer toward his customers. He doesn't consider them as human beings, but merely as dollar signs to ring up on his cash register. What does he care if a man goes home and beats his wife and children?

A little checking on my part with some of the men loitering near the clinic showed all too clearly that the four men had indeed been sold another jug of wine, and it was this jug that had become the passport to eternity for them.

My blood boiled as I contemplated the fatal apathy and the smug self-satisfaction that tolerates the existence of such conditions. When will people wake up to the fact that these booze joints are the greatest single cause of hideous sex crimes, acts of violence, and juvenile delinquency? They make no bones about selling liquor to minors. How subtle is the influence they have in spreading general disregard for all law! If there is any decency or spirituality in a community, these dives are a threat to all that is good and worth while.

But to return to Blackie, Slim, Fatso, and Red. All four of them had at one time or another been patients in the alcoholic clinic on East Fourth Street. All four had expressed a strong desire to stop drinking.

"I'll do anything to stop drinking, doctor!" Blackie had exclaimed fervently the day some friends had fished him out of a Fifth Street gutter. "I'll take antabuse or anything you say, doctor. I've got to stop drinking or it'll kill me!" The others were only slightly less vehement in their declarations.

"Well, now, Blackie, that's good that you want to stop drinking, and I'll do everything I can to help you; but, as I've told you dozens of times already, I can only show you the way to do it—the rest is up to you. Turn your life over to God. Lay all your sins and problems at His feet and say: 'Lord, I have made a miserable, complete failure of my life. I want You to take over now. I'm giving up all the bad habits that have been keeping me from closer communion with You. Take me, Lord, just as I am, and cleanse me and make a new man of me through Jesus Christ.'"

Blackie made the declaration with an earnest sincerity. He insisted that I give him the antabuse therapy, and from my experience with other alcoholic patients I knew that it might provide him with a temporary crutch until he grasped the spiritual side of the program. Therefore I assented and began the treatment.

Blackie stayed sober for four months—longer, by far, than he had ever stayed away from liquor for twenty years; but disturbing reports began to drift my way as some of Blackie's other activities were whispered about.

He was reported to have been seen in the constant company of a notorious woman of the streets; and one day, as I was leaving the clinic, I ran into Blackie and his hoydenish female companion. He looked embarrassed, but attempted, without much success, to appear nonchalant.

I spoke to him about the matter at the first opportunity. "Now, Blackie, I don't want you to think that I am interfering in your personal affairs," I began; "but you have repeatedly told me that you want to stay sober and turn your life over completely to God. When you do that, Blackie, it means a surrender of everything in your life that is in any way retarding your spiritual growth. I'll tell you frankly right now that you'll never stay on a spiritual program, or even keep your sobriety long, if you consort with loose women."

Blackie blushed in spite of himself. "You see, doctor," he began lamely, "Jean's an old friend of mine. I've known her for years; and when I used to get sick from the booze, she'd take care of me. I can't give an old friend like that the gate when I owe her so much. But I do intend to break it off as soon as I can without hurting her feelings."

"Listen, Blackie," I said earnestly, "there's nothing more important in your life right now than for you to stay sober and obey God's will for you. It's your only hope; you know that. You must not let anything get in your way that will keep you from doing this. You don't have to worry about hurting Jean's feelings. If you drop her, she'll have another sucker on the string within a few hours; you know that as well as I do. Let's get serious

about this and cut out all the self-deception and rational-
izing. What do you say?"

"O.K., doctor, I'll break off with her and really try to
give myself to God. I've tried everything else, and I'm
desperate. Believe me, doctor, I want to be a better man.
I'll do my best."

Brave words, Blackie; but, alas, human nature is so
weak! For a few weeks Blackie made a genuine effort to
keep out of Jean's way, but gradually he began to neglect
his daily prayers. Then he began to build up the resentments that are so fatal to the alcoholic. I heard him com-
plaining about his boss, his landlord, and even about his
friends. Not long afterward I encountered him drunk
on the street, back in the company of the notorious Jean.
She smirked as she started to pass me, and Blackie was too
far gone even to recognize me.

I stopped them. "Well, I see you've got Blackie back
where you want him," I said coldly. "If you had any
decency at all in your make-up you'd leave him alone.
You know he's trying to stay sober and get himself
straightened out, but it looks as though you're not satisfied
until you get him back in the gutter."

A sneer curled the hussy's painted lips. "Well, if it
ain't my psalm-singing doctor friend," she said insolently.
"If you'll hold still for a minute, I'll give you some news.
Blackie and I are going to get married. We love each
other, and he's sick and tired of trying to be a good boy.
He likes to drink, and so do I, and none of this religious
stuff is gonna change us, either," she ended defiantly. "So
why don't you leave us alone and go roll your pills?"

There was nothing to be gained by further argument

with this modern Jezebel, so I walked on with a heavy heart and a prayer that God would still save Blackie. As the days passed, Blackie continued on in the drunken course that was to be his last on earth. The poor fellow never really straightened up, and he finally passed beyond hope of return in the St. George Hotel fire.

Red Simpson was a case that had me baffled for some time. He did not have the obvious weaknesses that characterized Blackie's life. He gave Jean and her kind a wide berth and even tried to get Blackie to do the same.

"The woman is making a fool out of you!" I heard him telling Blackie one day. "Why don't you get smart and give her the gate? She's nothing but bad news from the word Go. If you want a girl friend, get a decent one."

It seemed obvious to me from these remarks, delivered as they were with considerable vehemence, that whatever Red's weakness might be, it wasn't loose women. But what was it? There was definitely something in his life that was keeping him from making a full surrender to God.

One day, as I paused in the clinic reading room, I saw Red intently poring over a magazine. So absorbed was he in whatever he was reading that he did not notice my presence until I had addressed him a couple of times.

"Must be pretty interesting stuff you're reading, Red," I remarked. "Now, if you'd give even a fraction of that same concentration and time to your Bible study, I'd feel a lot better about your chances of staying sober and changing your life."

I noticed that Red was trying to keep the magazine he had been reading out of my sight, but not before I had seen its title. It was called *Snappy Stories,* and its front cover portrayed a scantily clad woman and a man brandishing a gun. I went straight to the point.

"Red, I'm going to be frank with you. You say that you want to turn your life over to God and let Him take charge. You'll never be successful in doing so until you get rid of that trash you're reading. You've got to get rid of everything that stands between you and heaven. The lewd thoughts and acts portrayed in that trash you're reading lead to overt acts of wickedness. Can't you see that?"

"Aw, doctor, I only read this stuff for relaxation," he pleaded. "I don't take it serious; but if you say they're bad, I'll cut them out. I really want to stay sober and get on this spiritual program."

Again, brave words. Red could no more give up his salacious reading than Blackie could resist his women of easy virtue. He went on another drunk and ended his earthly career in the holocaust of smoke and flame at the St. George Hotel. Red had been offered salvation many times, but he failed to grasp it because he was unwilling to put aside the habits and desires that were the stumbling blocks in his life. He never learned that Jesus wants a full surrender of our lives when we come to Him.

Like Blackie and Red, the other two men also had longed for sobriety, but they also found it impossible to master personal habits. They all wanted sobriety, but their carnal desires were dearer to them than life itself. They refused to say: "Lord, take these desires out of my heart and make me after Thy likeness."

Chapter 7

Why They Fail

FOR many alcoholics the end of the trail comes in the crowded, noisome, littered streets and back alleys of some skid row. For some the descent to ragged, unshaven, tremulous winos is swift and dreadful. One day they are successful lawyers, bookkeepers, doctors, bankers, newspaper writers,—yes, even ministers of the gospel,—the next, they are nameless, faceless alcoholic nomads in an asphalt jungle. Some reach road's end more gradually, as their moral and spiritual values are insidiously and almost imperceptibly undermined by alcohol. They lose all that is finest in their God-given natures and find themselves engulfed in an alcoholic torrent that bears them irresistibly into the backwash of skid row.

Life for the alcoholic in the typical big-city skid row is no bed of roses. He finds himself kicked from pillar to post. He spends his waking hours almost exclusively in search of a bottle of cheap, poisonous wine. He sleeps in vermin-infested fifty-cent-a-night flophouses, and eats cheap, greasy, nonnourishing food at irregular intervals between drinking bouts.

He is fair game for the police who patrol skid row

continually and pick up derelicts such as he. Society shuns and scorns him as a weakling and a misfit. When he becomes ill from the cheap booze he has been drinking for weeks and even months, he finds himself in jail, or if he is luckier, in the charity ward of the county hospital. On all sides he is liable to encounter impatience, intolerance, and misunderstanding of his problem. He hasn't the funds to enter any high-priced sanitarium for a so-called alcoholic cure, and he has worn out his welcome at the emergency hospital and the various low-fee outpatient clinics. As his alcoholism intensifies, he becomes even more uncertain as to where to turn for help. He finds himself up against a blank wall, knowing not which way to turn for aid. He often reaches the point where suicide seems the only way out.

But shining like a beacon light in a world of fog is the charity alcoholic rehabilitation clinic. We who serve at such a clinic try to view the facts in a realistic manner. We know that the majority of the men seeking assistance at the clinic are alcoholics who have the hardest medical, social, and spiritual problems to be found anywhere. We expect many of the men seeking admittance to be drunk or sick from a prolonged use of alcohol. We expect them to be dirty, unshaven, tremulous, and often vermin-infested. These are conditions we must accept on skid row. But regardless of the degraded physical and mental condition of these men, we look at them, not as hopeless human derelicts beyond aid, but as souls created in God's image who may yet be restored to sobriety, usefulness, and communion with God through the saving power of Jesus Christ.

Many of these alcoholic patients are literally lifted out of the gutter into the hospital, taken back to the alcoholic ward, cleaned up, and put to bed. Here sedation is administered whenever necessary, under medical direction, and a high-vitamin diet prescribed in most instances.

All men admitted to the alcoholic ward are required to remain for at least seventy-two hours and, in the majority of instances, this is sufficient time for them to get rid of their jitters and recover their strength sufficiently by adequate rest and the eating of nourishing food to enable them to be transferred to a forty-bed dormitory upstairs. Here they are free to come and go as they please, the only proviso being that their attendance at all religious services is a "must." As they gradually gain strength and self-confidence, the clinic's employment service obtains remunerative work for them in mowing lawns, cleaning windows, painting, carpentering, and doing other odd jobs for housewives and businessmen.

Emphasis is laid continually on the necessity of each man's placing his problem completely in God's hands without mental reservations of any kind. The alcoholic is told repeatedly that it is only through the saving grace of Jesus Christ that he can ever hope to attain permanent sobriety and enjoy peace, serenity, and the sense of freedom from bondage.

About one hundred new alcoholic cases normally pass through the clinic's alcoholic ward each month, and I have opportunity to study and analyze the men, their histories, and the reasons why they do or don't get on the permanent spiritual program that constitutes their only hope of escaping from alcohol. From these observations

I have reached the conclusion that failure of the alcoholic to grasp a permanent spiritual solution to his problem is caused by one or more stumbling blocks.

The situation is rendered more complex by the fact that many of these alcoholics have actually achieved sobriety for periods of from one to ten years. A significant number of them have been members of Alcoholics Anonymous for many years; some have been sober after consultation with psychiatrists and other physicians; others are graduates of our charity clinic. But somewhere along the line they have refused to face the facts about something in their lives, and this has caused them to return to their drinking. The tragic part about this is that many of these alcoholics have virtually rebuilt their lives during their years of sobriety; they have returned to the affection and respect of their families; they have acquired property, have good positions in many instances, and have regained the confidence and respect of the community in which they live. All of this is swept away again by a series of drunken sprees.

One of the chief factors—the commonest and most insidious—is the unwillingness of the alcoholic to make a real change in habits and practices that produce a barrier to full acceptance of a spiritual outlook on life. Such habits and practices may have gone on for years in the person's experience.

Outwardly their lives appear to be changed for the better. They render lip service to God and seem to accept spiritual values, but in their hearts and in their minds they continue to nurture and cherish egotism, the desire for gratification of appetite, and the yearning for the empty pleasures that were major factors in the development of their alcoholism in the first place.

Harry K. had apparently accepted Jesus as his Saviour and was enthusiastic in his religious life. He did not hesitate to testify in public as to how he had been saved from alcohol, and he attended church regularly. He freely admitted his desperate condition prior to his acceptance of Christ. But Harry, in his drinking days, had developed a habit he didn't give up when he was sober. He had become accustomed to frequenting dance halls and night clubs. He would mingle with women and other worldly associates who were to be found in these places. He asked God to free him of his alcoholism, but in effect he also said: "God, rid me of this terrible drink habit, but let me continue to hang around these dance halls and night clubs that I enjoy so much." Poor Harry didn't realize, until he had gone on a drinking spree that left him without his car, home, or even his clothes, that God will not accept us on those terms, whether our problem is alcoholism or some other evil. At last he is beginning to learn that it is only by a complete and voluntary surrender of *everything* wrong that we can fully receive heaven's blessings. I have hopes that Harry will become a fervent worker for the Lord someday soon, as his attitude has changed.

Another major cause of the alcoholic's failure to achieve sobriety, or to retain it once he has achieved it, is the abuse of the physical powers of the body temple. It is only through our bodies that the mind and soul can reach their complete growth and attain their full potential for the grasping of things spiritual. Therefore when we do that which harms the body in any way we are in effect retarding our mental and spiritual growth. See 1 Corinthians 3:16, 17; 6:19, 20; 10:31.

Depraving appetites and defiling habits that befoul the body temple must be bridled and brought under the domination of the will, which in turn is to be at all times under the control of God's Holy Spirit.

George S., from early childhood, had acquired a habit only slightly less enslaving than the alcohol. He had a cigarette dangling from his lips almost continuously from morning to night.

The chief difference between the nicotine user and the alcoholic lies in the fact that the smoker of cigarette or cigar or pipe harms principally himself and does not constitute a social problem. The alcoholic, on the other hand, destroys not only himself, but brings misery and suffering to his family, friends, and loved ones. In addition, he constitutes a public-health problem—a social, medical, moral, and spiritual headache to all those with whom he comes in contact.

George realized after a time that tobacco was beclouding his mind, slowing his mental faculties, and impairing his digestion. But the grip of habit was so strong that he tried without avail to break it. Later, when he became an alcoholic, he merely added another body-and-mind-and-soul-destroying habit to his daily experience. Eventually he landed in our clinic in a sick condition. He listened attentively while I talked to him of things spiritual and of the necessity of his accepting Christ. He agreed that I was right, and together we knelt by his bedside and prayed for relief from the burden of his alcoholism.

But George wasn't honest with himself, with me, or with God. Mentally he resolved to turn his alcohol problem over to a "higher power" for solution, but, at the same time, in the recesses of his mind, he tried to rationalize that the cigarettes were all right. For a few months he managed to remain sober; but excessive smoking made him nervous and half nauseated when he arose in the mornings; and it was not long until George felt an overpowering need for an early-morning drink, or eye opener, to soothe his nicotine-jangled nerves. I scarcely need to tell the sequel to the story. To an alcoholic "one drink is too many, and a hundred aren't enough." George embarked on a spree that ended some weeks later back in our hospital ward. I pointed out the reason for his failure in this instance and emphasized, as I had with Harry, the absolute necessity of the alcoholic's giving up *everything* that retards his recovery from alcoholism. George accepted my advice and put his cigarette habit in God's hands. He tells me now that he doesn't even miss cigarettes.

It has long been known and recognized by the medical profession that tobacco, however used, is a slow-acting but insidious poison. It attacks the highest nerve centers, upsets the digestion, and, through irritation, causes excessive secretion of stomach acids which eat into the stomach lining and set up an almost irresistible craving for something stronger. In many instances this something stronger is alcohol, and the unfortunate victim of nicotine awakens one day to find himself saddled with another habit that will complete the ruin nicotine started.

Many reputable physicians, including those of the best clinics, refuse to begin treatment in cases of stomach ulcer unless there is complete abstinence from tobacco on the patient's part. Stomach ulcer, as well as alcoholism, is a condition in which extreme nervousness is a major causative factor. Tobacco puts the ulcer patient's nerves on edge so completely that recovery is almost impossible.

It has been my observation as a physician that the tobacco habit, excluding the social pressures to drink, is quite possibly *the* major factor in causing alcoholism in both men and women and in retarding their recovery from the drink habit once they have acquired it. While the alcoholic continues to smoke, he can never be sure he won't slip.

Closely allied to the use of nicotine as a factor in the causation of alcoholism is the use of cola drinks, tea, coffee, and highly seasoned, spicy foods. Coffee, as well as cola drinks and tea, will give its user a temporary lift. This is produced by caffeine, a powerful heart-and-nerve stimulant. But not long after the cup of coffee has been taken, a feeling of letdown comes, which the habitual coffee user offsets by the simple expedient of taking another cup of coffee. After a time this process goes on from morning until night; and when bedtime comes, the coffee addict is sometimes startled to find that he has consumed twenty cups of coffee that day. His nerves are jangled, his stomach is jittery from the irritating coffee oils he has put into it, and he is in no condition to get any restful sleep. He thinks longingly of another cup of coffee, but realizes that this will give him ease for but a few brief minutes. Alcohol—now that's something he has always heard to be an aid to slumber. He arises, proceeds to the nearest liquor store, and purchases a pint, or perhaps even a quart, of whisky or gin. He finds its initial effects so soothing and pleasant that he takes more and more until he blacks out in an alcoholic coma. In the morning he awakens with a hang-over, the result of his overindulgence in coffee and alcohol. This calls for more alcohol, and thus he is on his way to alcoholism.

As in the nicotine habit, already described, the alcoholic must learn to put aside the coffee and tea habits resolutely and firmly. He will probably need God's help in doing this, since these habits are only slightly less enslaving, in many cases, in their hold on the individual than is alcohol.

Highly seasoned and spicy foods inflame and irritate the delicate mucous membranes of throat, stomach, and intestines. Food that is prepared in accordance with sound health principles tastes flat and insipid. The tendency is ever toward something stronger and more stimulating, and this leads to the use of alcohol.

Barbiturates and other sedatives are an alluring, but especially dangerous, pitfall for the alcoholic seeking recovery. He finds that his nerves and stomach do not immediately behave as they did before he became an alcoholic, and they are liable to be jittery and tense. As he suffers from chronic alcoholic sleeplessness, he often seeks relief from these minor discomforts through the use of some form of the barbiturates, or, as they are more commonly known to alcoholics, "goof balls."

Many alcoholics who habitually use such sedatives delude themselves into thinking that they have achieved victory over alcoholism. Actually, however, they have merely substituted an even more destructive habit for the one they have put aside. Barbiturates, if used over a sufficiently prolonged period and in sufficient amounts, can cause brain damage and eventual insanity. Their use by alcoholics merely paves the way for a return to alcoholic degradation or worse.

The alcoholic must arouse himself to an awareness of the dangers inherent in these practices and must make a firm resolution to continue studying and practicing the principles of sane, healthful living. He must do this if he wishes to recover permanently from the alcohol habit that is destroying him.

It is true that the only permanent solution to the alcoholic's problem lies in his dependence on divine strength to break his appetite for liquor, but this by no means precludes the necessity for him to obey God's laws, both moral and physical.

The Bible tersely describes the love of money as "the root of all evil." Here again a pitfall yawns for the unwary alcoholic seeking relief from his condition. If he possesses this highly dangerous, obsessive love of money for itself, or for the luxuries it will bring, he has set up a false idol to worship instead of God. He is, in fact, in a worse condition than the pagan heathen who bows down to an idol of wood or stone, for he deliberately puts God out of his life. If he refuses to put aside this lust for lucre, it can be said, with much evidence to substantiate the point, that it will be only a matter of time until he resumes his alcoholic debauchery. There are numerous examples of rich men who have become chronic alcoholics and have taken their own lives when ultimately confronted with the emptiness of life. Many men come to our clinic who want to stay sober. They rush out to take a job that will interfere with their spiritual study and growth, and yet they hope to gain the victory over alcohol.

Other alcoholics fail to achieve permanent sobriety because they stop growing spiritually. In their first desperate plight they cry out to God sincerely and fervently for help. That is as it should be; but it is not enough. It is also essential for them to continue in this contrite, humble attitude of supplication to God. This can only be done through daily Bible study and continual prayer for heaven's wisdom and guidance.

Willard S., a one-time patient at our clinic, was an example of what happens to a man who fails to grow in spiritual experience. He was desperately sick from a prolonged bout with alcohol, and he got down on his knees and cried out to a "higher power" for relief from his condition. He believed that his prayer had been answered, and for a time he appeared to be free from the influence of liquor. But, in talking with him, I was astounded to find that he stubbornly refused to acknowledge the Bible truth that Christ died on Calvary. Willard soon returned to his old way of life. When I last heard of him, he had been committed to a state institution for treatment.

The declaration of belief in a "higher power," followed by a stubborn refusal to identify that power with God and Jesus Christ, is a highly dangerous evasion of truth which, for the alcoholic, is tantamount to destruction.

By this time it should be clear why it is so essential that the alcohol addict turn his problem over entirely to God; life for him has turned into a seemingly endless series of perils that threaten from all sides. Through his reckless indulgence of an illicit appetite, he has literally placed himself beyond human aid. He has reached "the point of no return," where he is faced with two alternatives: He either turns his problem over to God for solution or tries to solve it by human means. One way means a useful, sober, happy life; the other will bring certain misery, remorse, despair, and ultimate death, both physically and spiritually.

In closing this chapter I can do little more than name a few of the remaining causative factors for the "slips" that come to alcoholics. These are, in reality, the inevitable outcome of a refusal on the part of the alcoholic to recognize his own and his fellow man's inability to help him unless he first turns to God.

Resentments. The typical alcoholic develops and nurtures resentments, hatreds, and jealousies which are often highly imaginative. He may be against his wife, family friends, business associates, and, in fact, about anyone and everyone. Unless he rids himself of these through prayer, he is doomed to a return to alcoholism. If we follow Christ's instruction to pray for those who despitefully use us, our resentment or hatred will turn into love and pity for our enemies.

Holding Mental Reservations Concerning His Drinking. Many alcoholics fail to make the grade because they stubbornly cling to the belief—seldom openly expressed—that, someday, somehow, they will again be able to take a drink without fateful consequences. They hang on to this destructive belief even in the face of insanity and death. The unalterable medical truth is that once a person

crosses the paper-thin barrier between normal and abnormal drinking, he can never learn to control it again.

Suggestive Literature, Movies, Television, Dancing.
Anything that arouses lustful thoughts and desires in the
human mind is undesirable and abhorrent to the Christian. This can be especially harmful to one possessing
alcoholic tendencies, since the close relationship existing
between lust and liquor is well known. Some of the
motion pictures, television programs, and literature of
today are cesspools of filth that have no place in a Christian life. Dancing, because of the inevitable close contact
between the two sexes, should be strictly avoided by the
alcoholic. My observation of many alcoholic cases leads
me to believe that, while alcoholics should help other
alcoholics achieve sobriety, it is a highly dangerous practice for a male alcoholic to try to help a female alcoholic,
and vice versa (married couples excepted). Failure to
follow this simple, common-sense rule has been the down-
fall of alcoholics of both sexes seeking sobriety. Any
association that may lead to the violation of the seventh
commandment should be avoided at all costs. Unholy
sex desires are a major factor in the failure of alcoholics
to return to sobriety. The psalmist says truly: "If I regard
iniquity in my heart, the Lord will not hear me." Psalm
66:18. The solution is for the alcoholic to lay the sex
problem, when it comes, in God's hands, with repeated,
heartfelt prayer.

Braggadocio Concerning Past Life. Too many alcoholics, after an initial period of sobriety, are likely to
recall, nostalgically, incidents of their alcoholic pasts that
would best be buried and forgotten. When offered even

the slightest encouragement, they do not hesitate to speak publicly of their past drinking prowess, sexual irregularities, and other alcoholic eccentricities. Such experiences should only be confessed to God in prayer.

Pride. After only a few months of sobriety, some alcoholics are inclined to boast of their accomplishments. "See what I've done in the few months I've been sober," they say, forgetting that it is only because of God's grace that they are sober for a moment. It is only through utter distrust of self, and complete and lasting dependence on God, that the alcoholic can stand.

Development of a Selfish Attitude. Some alcoholics take the position that their sobriety is the only important thing in the world. They fail to see that it is also their concern to help their fellow sufferers come back from alcoholism. Wrapped up in their own selfishness, they say, like Cain of old, "Am I my brother's keeper?" This attitude can easily become a two-edged sword that will attack its user. By helping his fellow alcoholic and by educating youth concerning the dangers of alcohol, he is merely working out his own salvation.

Bad Company. An alcoholic should be careful at all times to avoid bad companions of both sexes and, in fact, should not unnecessarily put himself in the company of those who lack a devout Christian experience. This applies especially to recovered alcoholics who are seeking life companions.

Stumbling Blocks. Some individuals, through spurious, insincere, spiritual experience which they undergo "with tongue in cheek," are able to be sober for weeks or even years. Others, by even more dubious therapies, manage somehow to maintain an unstable and purely temporary term of sobriety. During this uneasy and usually unhappy period of "dry drunkenness," as it is generally termed by other ex-alcoholics, these men and women continue to smoke, indulge their passions, and in general behave as though they have no alcohol problem. Other alcoholics to whom indulgence in behavior of this type is fatal almost at once to their sobriety, attempt to emulate these superficial people, with disastrous consequences. Within a short period of time they have resumed their heavy and uncontrolled drinking. No words of mine are strong enough to condemn the thoughtless actions and the evil example set by these "dry drunks." The only safe policy for the alcoholic is to allow these shallow, self-deluded men and women to go their own way to ultimate disaster. He must concentrate on maintaining his own sobriety through the methods outlined in this book.

Gambling, swearing, the telling of smutty stories, and a failure to take a positive stand on the evils of liquor are other sources of danger to the alcoholic seeking sobriety. Let me repeat that the alcoholic who sincerely and contritely turns his problem over to God and who maintains daily contact with heaven through prayer and Bible study, is a man or woman well on the way to full recovery from this malignant illness of body, mind, and spirit.

Chapter 8

How You Can Help

IT IS doubtful if there is a subject more mis-understood than is alcoholism, or that has more ignorance connected with it. The widespread lack of knowledge of the true nature of alcoholism is rendered even more tragic when we stop to consider that this disease, for such it is now generally recognized to be, is one of the leading public-health problems confronting our nation today.

This dismal state of affairs is not confined to the un-educated. Intelligent businessmen, educators, social work-ers, yes, and even representatives of the clergy and medical fraternity, are found to be woefully lacking in knowledge of this problem.

Harry J., a chronic alcoholic of many years' standing, had tried for a long time to curtail the excessive drinking that was ruining his life and bringing misery to his family. He tried all the standard cures for his condition—psychiatry, the "alcoholic aversion" treatment, antabuse, and confinement in a state hospital. Finally some inter-ested and well-meaning friend told him that his only hope of achieving permanent sobriety lay in his acceptance of a religious program. Harry made an appointment without delay to talk the matter over with his pastor. This gentleman occupied a position of importance in the community as the pastor of a large church. He was regarded as a leader in civic affairs, enjoying the reputation of being a wise counselor in the marital problems and everyday affairs of his flock.

Harry entered Reverend Smith's study with high hopes, but he emerged an hour later disillusioned and in a frame of mind to start out on an alcoholic spree. The Reverend Smith, it seemed, had taken almost the entire time of the interview to give Harry a "raking over the coals." He had made no secret of the fact that he regarded Harry's case as hopeless and that, since Harry had chosen to disregard the temperance Sunday-school lessons to which he had been exposed as a boy, there wasn't anything that could be done to help him.

I haven't the slightest doubt that the worthy pastor thought he had done the best thing for the errant member of his flock; but, actually, he could hardly have pursued a more disastrous course. By his brusque and thoughtless handling of a delicate situation, he had succeeded only in thoroughly alienating a desperately sick man from his only remaining hope of salvation; he had badly muffed an opportunity that the understanding Christian should grasp and turn to good advantage for the Lord. He did not see the significance of the Biblical passage: "Wherefore He is able also to save them to the uttermost that come unto God by Him, seeing He ever liveth to make intercession for them."

George Carlson was another man whose alcoholism had brought him to the verge of suicide. He had become a problem to his family, his friends, and to the various relief agencies in his home town. He was well known to the police department as a result of having been picked up in a helpless drunken condition on numerous occasions. Someone referred him to a prominent doctor in town whose reputation as a physician and surgeon would cause one to expect to receive a sympathetic and understanding attitude on the alcohol question. However, this eminent member of the medical profession, after listening with ill-concealed impatience to George's story of alcoholic frustration and despair, interrupted the recital abruptly. Reaching back of him to a small table, he picked up a Colt automatic and said, "That's the only cure I know of for alcoholism, Mr. Carlson. Frankly, I think you are a hopeless case, and I would recommend that you commit yourself to the state hospital for an indefinite stay."

Here again the door had been callously slammed on the last flickering hope of an alcoholic desperately seeking help.

The alcoholic who is desperately striving with his uncontrollable appetite for liquor can take renewed hope in the fact that God does not regard even the most confirmed alcoholic as hopeless. Therefore, to the Christian worker, no alcoholic but a dead one, or one who has been committed to an insane asylum with a permanent alcoholic psychosis, is to be regarded as beyond help.

God knows all the circumstances, all the temptations, all the weaknesses of character. He knows the inherited tendencies to evil that beset the alcoholic. He views them with all the love and understanding pity for mankind's foibles and weaknesses that induced Him to send His only Son to the cross of Calvary that we might have eternal life. Therefore, in view of Christ's example, one of the first lessons to be learned by the person trying to help an alcoholic recover from his illness is that no case is hopeless.

As the alcoholic you are trying to help gradually becomes aware of his degraded condition and as he begins to suffer the remorse and self-accusation that follow such a discovery, you must make every effort within your power to make him feel that you are his friend. Whatever you do, never berate or censure the actions of the alcoholic you are trying to help. Remember, at this stage of his alcoholism he is well aware of the tragic consequences of his drinking, and he is already giving himself so much mental punishment that your additional scolding may well result in his attempting to drown his remorse in the only way he knows—by drinking more liquor.

Talk courage to him. Make him realize that the Father loves him in spite of all his shortcomings. He may be ashamed; but stress the fact that, as he confesses his faults, God is faithful and just to forgive him and to cleanse him from all unrighteousness.

Open the Bible before the tempted, struggling alcoholic. Read the heartening promises to be found there. Show him that by trusting in these promises he will receive power to obey God's commandments. If he falls again, do not become discouraged. Remember, it has probably taken years of excessive drinking and twisted thinking to bring him to his present state; it will take time and patience to bring him back to sobriety and communion with God.

It is even possible that you will suffer deep hurt or humiliation because of the actions of the alcoholic you are trying to help. Under such conditions you may be tempted to wash your hands of the entire affair and do nothing further for him. In doing so, however, you will be disregarding the admonition of Jesus to forgive until seventy times seven.

Instead of admitting defeat, you can attempt to convince the alcoholic that he not only can, but that he must, resist temptation. Stress the fact that those who put their trust in Christ can never be held in bondage by any debasing appetite or passion. Remember, too, that you cannot do it all for him; he must be convinced of the necessity to work in his own behalf. Stress the fact that there is a great difference between the man who genuinely serves God and the one who does not. When the alcoholic makes up his mind to serve God, then and only then can God's grace begin to work for him.

The husband or wife, sweetheart, relative, or friend of an alcoholic should realize at the outset that the task may be a long, uphill, and often disheartening one. The behavior of the typical alcoholic is usually eccentric. He is moody, unreliable, tricky, and untruthful where alcohol is concerned. He is contrite and remorseful at times, but vain and boastful at others. Medically, socially, and spiritually, the treatment and rehabilitation of the average alcoholic is admittedly a problem both complex and difficult. Efforts to guide the alcoholic to God will be greatly enhanced if the worker is a devout Christian. If he lacks this, but is sincere in his efforts to help the alcoholic, he should lose no time in becoming a genuine, active Christian. This can best be done through a careful and searching study of the Bible. For workers in this category, we suggest enrollment in the Introductory Bible Lessons for Alcoholics offered at the end of this book. It has been found through long experience that the Christian principles of love, long-suffering, tolerance, and forgiveness are invaluable attributes in dealing with the alcoholic. For a person without any real knowledge of the Bible to attempt to bring an alcoholic to God is but another example of the blind leading the blind.

It must be remembered that the alcoholic should be treated with firmness at times, but this should be mixed with wisdom and tenderness, since the typical alcoholic is a sensitive individual who is easily hurt by real or imagined slights, criticism, or by the unfortunate tendency of some people to talk down to the alcoholic as though he were a child.

On the other hand, it is as easy to fail to help the alcoholic because one adopts an opposite course. It is fully as fatal to flatter and praise the alcoholic who has achieved a few months of sobriety as it is to sneer at his efforts. By lavishing extravagant praise, you may cause him to believe that he has the power within himself to stop his drinking. He forgets conveniently that the credit belongs to God, and that the moment he takes his eyes off Jesus and begins to rely on his own feeble efforts, he will once more revert to his old life of soddenness and sin.

The popular practice of having alcoholics give public testimonies, often in lurid detail, of their former sinful lives is one that is fraught with dire consequences for both the testifier and his listeners. No conceivable good can come from dwelling on past scenes of unbridled lust and uncontrolled appetite; yet this practice continues to receive unqualified approval in certain quarters, possibly because of the vicarious thrills it provides for a jaded and blasé segment of the audience.

It should be understood by the reader that the author is in no way criticizing genuine Christian testimonies of what God's power has done in lives, for thereby great and lasting good is often accomplished. Instead of indulging in harmful reminiscences over past follies, the alcoholic genuinely interested in attaining permanent sobriety and struggling desperately to gain a true spiritual experience, will find it infinitely more rewarding to place himself in the company of experienced Christians. By such association he will acquire the added spiritual strength so necessary for lasting victory. It is not unreasonable to assume that God will touch the hearts of the devout Christians with whom the alcoholic places himself and that they will do all they can to help him win the victory.

The alcoholic who is not as yet interested in getting well, or who stubbornly refuses all spiritual aid, or who declines to discuss the spiritual side of life, presents a difficult problem to those who seek to help him. Any attempt to force religious beliefs upon him only results in making him retreat further and further from God and to bar him from the only cure for his alcoholism.

When a direct attempt to induce an alcoholic to turn his life over to Christ appears to be doomed to failure, success can sometimes be surprisingly attained by following the apostle Paul's example. He says, "Being crafty, I caught you with guile."

The case of Walter H. illustrates one way in which an enterprising businessman made a practical application of harmless subterfuge to accomplish something which would surely have failed in a direct attack. Walter had an alcoholic wife who adamantly refused to face the facts and admit her condition. She refused point blank to discuss her problem, which she maintained, even in the face of overwhelming evidence, was no problem at all. She particularly resisted any attempt to consider spiritual matters, and, for a long time, Walter felt that he had reached an impasse in his efforts to help her.

However, Walter was a resourceful person, and he finally hit upon a plan that was simple and effective. He telephoned his wife one day from his office, expressing great concern for some papers he said he had mislaid somewhere at home. He subtly hinted that they might be in the desk in his den. After considerable rummaging around in the desk, Walter's wife was unable to locate the allegedly missing papers; but she did run across a copy of *Listen* magazine which, by curious coincidence, contained an article on alcoholism entitled "Thirteen Years in Hell." The woman read the article avidly and forgot all about her husband's missing papers. Many of the incidents related in the article struck home to her, and she realized, in a sudden burst of insight, not only that she was an alcoholic, but that her only hope for permanent recovery lay in a full surrender to Jesus. As a result of her husband's resourcefulness, she is now making good progress in her recovery from alcoholism.

While we may not all be fortunate enough to be given an opportunity such as Walter H.'s, we can make it a practice to leave helpful books and pamphlets on the alcohol problem in places where they will come to the alcoholic's attention. Free from any feeling that he is being high-pressured into something he doesn't want, the alcoholic, in many instances, will accept counsel which he feels he has discovered. In fact, it is highly desirable for the alcoholic to reach his own conclusion concerning the nature of his problem. The turning point in his career is reached only when he voluntarily admits that he needs and desires help. The decision must be his own, and it must be made without coercion.

Among the strongest Don'ts to be kept in mind by those seeking to help the alcoholic is the one relating to the encouragement of his or her drinking. Many wives who are total abstainers themselves, under the entirely mistaken impression that they are helping to curb their husbands' drinking, serve liquor in the home. Their theory is that, if he must drink, it is preferable to have him do so under their watchful eye and not in some saloon or dive. In rare instances this plan may appear to bring results; but in the long run the alcoholic sees through his wife's ruse, and his eventual resentment at being duped serves as an excuse for heavier drinking. A wife who goes even further than this and joins her husband in his drinking is not only actively aiding and abetting him in his alcoholism, but she may quite possibly be in danger of becoming an alcoholic herself.

In certain extreme instances it may be necessary for the one who is helping an alcoholic to take drastic measures. Where the personal safety of a wife or child is endangered by a drunken husband, the only sensible course to pursue is to call in the police. Such an action may alienate the person from the one he is seeking to help, but this is unavoidable under such circumstances. However, it may have an entirely opposite effect by rudely jolting him to his senses and making him realize the true seriousness of his condition.

When drastic action is considered the only method left to use in dealing with an alcoholic, threats of extreme measures should never be made unless there is a willingness and an intention to carry them out. Idle threats serve merely to estrange the alcoholic from the person working in his behalf, without accomplishing any good. If no action is really intended, it is better to say nothing. When drastic action has been taken, with a resulting resentment, the worker should seek by every reasonable means possible to regain the alcoholic's confidence.

An example of the wrong approach to the solution of an alcoholic's problem where drastic action was necessary, is the case of Edward G., an alcoholic who for many years had dissipated his life savings through his uncontrolled drinking. He succeeded in inducing his skeptical son and daughter-in-law to allow him to live with them. He managed to do so during one of his periods of sobriety, and only after fervid protestations and vows to refrain from ever drinking again. After a few weeks of "nibbling" at the bottle, he came home in the early hours to the respectable neighborhood in which his son and daughter-in-law lived. He was so under the influence of liquor that when he was unable to find his key to gain entrance he became violent, shouting loud and abusive language, which ended by kicking and hammering at the front door until he had aroused almost the entire neighborhood.

The painful morning-after scene found Edward remorseful and penitent, full of tearful pleas for "another chance." This was finally granted to him by his son over the protests of the son's wife.

A second short interval of strained sobriety was followed by a similar incident even more outrageous than the first. This time Edward was granted no leniency; he was ordered from the premises under threat of arrest. His son and daughter-in-law made it clear that they disowned him and would never even speak to him again. Although the man's actions certainly merited drastic action of some sort, failure on the part of his son and daughter-in-law to work out a less severe solution swept away any chance there might once have been to reclaim his life through an intelligent, sympathetic, but firm approach. Totally deserted by the only loved ones he had in the world, he allowed himself to sink into an alcoholic abyss from which it will be extremely difficult to ever escape.

A much more sensible course in Edward G.'s case would have been to have made it clear to him that he was a welcome guest at his son's house any time he was sober, but that a call would be made to the police any time he arrived in a drunken condition. Arrangements to house and feed him in another part of town on a much lower economic level would have made him realize realistically, but without brutality, that his son and daughter-in-law thoroughly disapproved of his actions, yet still maintained some filial affection. Such a solution would have made it much easier to reach the man with a telling argument for sobriety, since he would still be in possession of a certain measure of self-respect.

In dealing with alcoholics it is often necessary first to attend their physical needs. After a prolonged alcoholic spree many of them are in dire need of medical treatment for incipient delirium tremens, vitamin deficiencies, acute alcoholic gastritis, and tremors. Until these ailments have received proper attention, it is futile for the alcoholic worker to attempt rehabilitation.

Those who have been totally abandoned by their loved ones and friends usually are in immediate need of a bath, clean clothing, lodging, and good food. The ideal way to deal with indigent alcoholics would be to remove them from the adverse skid-row environment. This could best be done by a concerted effort on the part of Christian people to purchase and maintain rehabilitation farms strategically located a few miles from our great cities and their disgraceful slum areas. Such farms would in no wise be penal in their nature. They would be operated by the donations of civic-minded businessmen and Christian groups along lines similar to those now being used in the charity alcoholic rehabilitation clinic in Los Angeles. The farm produce raised through the voluntary efforts of the patients would help make such a project practically self-supporting.

For the most favorable results, the patient would remain on the farm for from two to three months and during that time would be exposed to the same religious therapy now being used with encouraging results at the clinic. The farms would have the advantage of removing alcoholics far from the ever-present temptations of wicked cities, and they would encourage alcoholics to seek God through honest toil and communion with nature.

The following statement by a well-known Christian writer should bring renewed hope and courage to us in concerted efforts for these unfortunate victims of alcohol. Ellen G. White has said:

"Nothing is apparently more helpless, yet really more invincible, than the soul that feels its nothingness, and relies wholly on the merits of the Saviour. By prayer, by the study of His word, by faith in His abiding presence, the weakest of human beings may live in contact with the living Christ, and He will hold them by a hand that will never let go."

Chapter 9

Today Is the Day

I REMEMBER the day as though it were yesterday. It was a bright, typically sunshiny Hawaiian day,
with a blue, cloudless sky above and the soft trade wind
rustling the palm trees lazily. I was standing by the
window of my office near famous Waikiki Beach. As I
looked at the peaceful scene, it was hard for me to realize
that we were at war with Japan. A group of Hawaiian,
Japanese, and Portuguese youngsters were noisily playing
football in the small park alongside my office. Some
myna birds, the chatterboxes of the bird world, were
having a domestic squabble of their own in a nearby palm
tree. Scantily clad men and women were beginning to
stroll toward the nearby beach to idle away the hours of
their "day off" from war work.

My thoughts were suddenly interrupted by the appearance of my office nurse, a smiling, pleasant-faced Japanese
girl, who had been with me for many years.

"This is Mr. Caesar, doctor," she announced. "He
called up yesterday and made an appointment for ten
o'clock this morning."

I glanced curiously at my visitor. He was an unusually

tall man—I should judge him to be at least six feet three—and he possessed a strikingly handsome, mobile face which was accentuated by his dark, curly hair and a pair of the bluest eyes I can remember seeing.

"Sit down, please, Mr. Caesar," I said, indicating a chair on the opposite side of my desk. "What seems to be the trouble?"

I had already noticed that he appeared to be in a highly nervous condition and that as he sat down and placed his hands on my desk, they shook. I studied him more closely. Certainly he didn't fit into the pattern of the popular conception of an alcoholic; he was well-dressed, clean-shaven, and his face showed few signs of prolonged alcoholic excess. Yet it was hard to disregard those tremulous hands and his quick, jumpy movements. I decided to take a shot in the dark.

"A little too much to drink, Mr. Caesar?" I began tentatively. "Well, that's become almost an occupational hazard here in Hawaii since the war, hasn't it?"

He didn't answer immediately, but I noticed that he had colored slightly at my query and that he wore a slightly sheepish, half-ashamed smile on his handsome face.

"Yeah, I guess that's about it, doctor," he said slowly. "You know how it is in Hawaii nowadays. Everyone's working under terrific pressure, and a drink or two allows a fellow to relax."

"I fear that that argument doesn't impress me much, Mr. Caesar," I replied shortly. "You see, not only do I hear it every day and sometimes several times a day, but it will not hold together when you examine it. For instance, you say that 'a drink or two' allows a man to relax. Now, it's quite apparent to me, without anything but a superficial examination, that last night you had considerably more than one or two drinks. Am I right?"

He nodded mutely, the same sheepish half smile on his face.

"All right. Now for point 2," I continued relentlessly. "I seriously question any relaxing qualities or virtues claimed for liquor, be it beer, wine, gin, whisky, or any other form of alcohol. Remember, alcohol is first, last, and always a deceiver. While it may appear to provide relaxation to the nerves in its initial effects, in reality it merely anesthetizes the higher nerve centers and thereby relieves you temporarily of any sense of pain or fatigue in the same manner as would ether.

"Point No. 3, Mr. Caesar, is this: I realize that you and thousands of others of us here in Hawaii, including myself, are working under terrific pressure. But do you think you are helping the war effort by getting yourself into your present condition? Suppose I couldn't give you anything to help you get straightened out. You wouldn't be able to go to work tomorrow, would you?"

My visitor shook his head. "I see your point, doctor; believe me, I do. I'm going to cut out this foolishness. You see," he went on in an almost apologetic tone, "I'm single, and I live in a housing area near Pearl Harbor. There are 350 of us men crowded like sardines into that barracks building; and with the black-out curfew at seven-thirty at night and no recreational facilities, no feminine companionship except what we can find around the bars in Honolulu, and the seven-day week we are working; well, things get pretty dull sometimes, and we have to break loose to keep from blowing our tops. I only drink on my days off, doctor; but I must admit that I seem to be drinking more than I should lately."

"Yes, and you'll find that you'll keep on drinking more and more if you don't do something about it right now. Alcoholism is a progressively deteriorating disease. Many a chronic alcoholic, wandering hopelessly on some city skid row today, started his drinking career in precisely the same way as you are drinking now."

Caesar gave a quick, nervous laugh. "Now, really, doctor, you're not going to tell me I'm an alcoholic, are you? I'll freely admit I have more than is good for me occasionally, as I did last night; but you'll never catch me taking a drink the morning after. Isn't there something you can give me now to help me over these jitters?"

"Yes, I can give you something that will calm you down and help you regain your appetite; but take my advice, Mr. Caesar, and leave this booze strictly alone. It's worse than tampering with TNT."

A few moments later my visitor left, and in the hectic days that followed—crowded hours, confusion, frustration, and the perpetual race against time—I forgot about Mr. Caesar.

About two weeks later, as I was closing my office for the day, Mr. Caesar was ushered in again. This time there was no doubt as to the cause of his sickness. He was pale, with beads of sweat on his forehead. A heavy, black stubble of beard darkened his face, and his clothes were unpressed and disheveled. His eyes were bloodshot and wild.

"Doctor, I really need your help this time," he gasped,

sinking limply into a chair. "I feel as though I'm going to collapse."

"You're in bad shape," I agreed; "and as I indicated last time you were here, you're fast becoming a borderline alcoholic case. A few more binges like this one and you'll find yourself hooked, as surely as the lowest skid-row derelict. Now, Mr. Caesar, what do you propose doing about your predicament?"

My visitor mopped the beads of cold sweat from his forehead before replying. "I realize I gotta do something, doctor," he said slowly. "I can feel the liquor getting a stronger grip on me all the time. You see, almost everyone out at the barracks is a drinking man, and it's a hard proposition to turn down offers to drink."

"Do you believe in God, Mr. Caesar?" I asked suddenly. "Do you believe that His Son, Jesus Christ, died on Calvary so that you and I might have eternal life?"

"Why, yes; I believe that, doctor," he replied, a puzzled frown creasing his brow at the unxpected turn our conversation was taking; "but I don't—"

"You don't see what that has to do with your drinking problem; is that it?" I asked.

"Well, yes, doctor; I don't quite get the tie-up," he answered slowly.

"When you do, your troubles will be over. You will solve not only your alcoholism, but also any other trouble or problem you may have," I replied. "Now, you may think what I am going to say is strange coming from a physician, but it's true. No doctor on earth, no psychiatrist, no hospital or sanitarium, no human agency,—in short, none of these,—can cure your drinking. But if you will take the few simple steps I am going to outline you'll find your problem a thing of the past. Sounds fantastic, doesn't it?" I noted the look of bewilderment on my visitor's face change to incredulity.

"What's the gag, doctor?" he queried. "Frankly, I don't get it. You say in one breath that no doctor can cure an alcoholic. Then you say that by following a few simple steps I can be cured."

"Yes, I understand your bewilderment," I answered; "but listen closely and I'll give you a formula for success that's worth more money to you than there is in the world. If you will get down on your knees and ask God for help, laying all perplexities, fears, and troubles before Him, He will lift the burden from you and make you free as you have never been before. This isn't a mere theory or fancy of mine, Mr. Caesar. I have proved it in my own life. Now, I don't use alcohol, but I have other problems that might soon back me up against a wall if I didn't make a practice of turning them over to God. I do this every day through prayer. If it works for me, it'll work for you. Are you willing to give it a trial?"

"Why, yes, doctor," he replied, somewhat dubiously; "I'll try anything once. I'm a desperate man, and I can't afford to pass up anything that may help me."

"All right, there's no better time than the present to start getting that help. Let's kneel here now and humbly ask God to remove your burden. Hold nothing back."

I prayed first and asked God to help my friend and patient as he struggled against the evil influence growing in his life. Then it was my patient's turn, and I was astounded at the depth of feeling, sincerity, and genu-

8—E.A.

ine anguish that poured out of his heart to his Maker.

When he had finished, his face was wet with tears, and I found, somewhat to my surprise, that my eyes, too, were moist with emotion. Seldom in my career have I seen a human soul laid bare in such a fashion.

"Doctor, do you know, I feel better already," he exclaimed, as we resumed our seats. "I believe that God heard my prayer and is beginning to answer it already."

"You must continue to pray daily," I said. "Make it a practice to start the day with prayer, and also pray whenever you feel the need for guidance, comfort, and strength, no matter where you may be. Now, I'm going to give you something to help you get shipshape again; but, remember, the thing that's going to do you more good than all the medicine in the world is daily prayer to God. Before you go, I want you to take this little book along. Read it when you have a few spare moments, and let me know what you think of it. Drop in and see me again in about a week. I'll be praying for you, too."

I handed him a copy of *David Dare,* a publication I have found invaluable as an opening wedge to develop faith in the Bible. Clasping the hand he pressed into mine, I bade him good-by.

I thought of Mr. Caesar often during the week, wondering what progress he was making and what impact, if any, *David Dare* was having upon him. I found myself waiting for his return with a sense of anticipation.

Promptly on the day and at the hour appointed, Mr. Caesar put in his appearance. Once again he was his old well-dressed, urbane self; but the telltale tremor of his hands was still in evidence.

"Say, doctor, that's a wonderful book!" he greeted me enthusiastically. "I don't know when I've read anything that fascinated me more. It explains a whole lot of things in the Bible that have puzzled me for years. The boys at the barracks beg me to let them read it, and I've already had a dozen arguments about it. Last night I thought Curly and Hardrock—they're two of the boys in the barracks with me—were going to swap punches over the question of the 'red horse' and the 'pale horse' in the book of the Revelation. Curly thought the red horse must represent Russia; Hardrock had another theory and, as for me, I didn't know what to think for sure. Frankly, the whole thing is confusing to all of us. Don't you have any other book that will explain in simple language the book of the Revelation? What we want is a book that will give references from recognized authorities and show how history is fulfilled in the Bible. Is there such a book, doctor?" he ended eagerly, edging forward on his chair awaiting an answer.

"There most certainly is, Mr. Caesar," I replied, delighted with his enthusiasm. "It is a book called *The Prophecies of Daniel and the Revelation,* and I think you will find it as engrossing as the booklet you have just finished. It's quite deep, I warn you, for a beginning Bible student. However, you are more than welcome to try your hand at it. In the meantime, here are a few extra copies of *David Dare* to distribute among the boys in the barracks so they'll all have a chance to read it without having to wait so long for their turn. Now, how's your drinking?" I asked.

"Under control, doctor," he replied. "I've made up my

mind I'll never allow myself to get into the same shape I was the last time you saw me."

"I won't try to pretend that I'm not disappointed, Mr. Caesar," I replied. "I hoped you'd be ready to make a full surrender to God. I believe you are convinced that it's the only way; but like so many other people today, you are putting it off until a later date."

"Yes, doctor, I'm convinced that God is the only answer for me," he agreed; "but it's awfully hard to stay away from liquor and gambling in a place like that barracks I'm in. As soon as the war's over, though, and things begin getting back to normal, I'll start going to church and really clean up my life."

I realized the futility of further argument, but I also sensed that God was working with my patient. I handed Mr. Caesar a copy of *The Prophecies of Daniel and the Revelation* and said, "Let me know how you like this book."

Another two weeks went by, and Mr. Caesar came back. "Doctor, that book is wonderful!" he exclaimed as soon as we had exchanged formal greetings. "Now I can understand things in the Bible that have been meaningless to me until you lent me that book. There's no doubt in my mind now but that the Bible is the inspired word of God."

I had been listening to his enthusiastic words with mounting hope. I wanted to hear him say he had read something that convinced him to turn his life over to God.

My patient seemed to read my thoughts. "I'm still drinking, doctor," he said quietly. "But, do you know something? Whatever enjoyment I used to get out of it, or imagined I did, is getting less and less all the time."

"I'm not going to say anything more about it, Mr. Caesar," I answered. "You know what you have to do to make your problem a thing of the past. I can only hope you'll take that step before it is too late."

On his next two visits, Mr. Caesar's enthusiasm for the prophecies had increased. "It's the most remarkable book I've ever read outside of the Bible," he exclaimed. "Every night now out at the barracks we have discussions on what we are reading. I let some of the other fellows read the book while I'm working, and it's being passed all around."

I didn't broach the matter of drinking again until the day Mr. Caesar said he had completed the book.

"Beware of procrastination," I told him. "The Bible says plainly, '*Now* is the day of salvation.' Let me read you a few words on this subject from another fine book called *Steps to Christ*. Listen to this:

" 'Do not put off the work of forsaking your sins, and seeking purity of heart through Jesus. Here is where thousands upon thousands have erred, to their eternal loss. I will not here dwell upon the shortness and uncertainty of life; but there is a terrible danger—a danger not sufficiently understood—in delaying to yield to the pleading voice of God's Holy Spirit, in choosing to live in sin; for such this delay really is. Sin, however small it may be esteemed, can be indulged in only at the peril of infinite loss. What we do not overcome, will overcome us, and work out our destruction. . . .

" 'Every act of transgression, every neglect or rejection of the grace of Christ, is reacting upon yourself; it is hardening the heart, depraving the will, benumbing the understanding, and not only making you less inclined to yield, but less capable of yielding, to the tender pleading of God's Holy Spirit. Many are quieting a troubled conscience with the thought that they can change a course of evil when they choose; that they can trifle with the invitations of mercy, and yet be again and again impressed. They think that after doing despite to the Spirit of grace, after casting their influence on the side of Satan, in a moment of terrible extremity they can change their course. But this is not so easily done.'"

My patient listened silently, but attentively, as I read. When I had finished, there was complete silence in the room for a few moments.

"Doctor, that's wonderful!" he exclaimed. "Could I possibly borrow that book, too? I don't want to impose on your good nature, but I am getting a lot of good out of everything you give me."

"Certainly, take this copy along and read it carefully. It contains advice which, if followed, will change your life completely." Little did I think, as I said those words, that they held a prophecy that was soon to be fulfilled.

It was only a week later that Mr. Caesar literally burst into my office. He was plainly under conviction. "Doctor, I'm going to give my heart to God and change my way of life, and I mean right now, too!" he blurted out as soon as I had closed the door to my office and we were alone.

"I've finished reading that wonderful book, *Steps to Christ,* and I never realized before what a great sinner I am! Do you really think there's any chance that Christ can ever forgive some of the things I've done?"

There was absolutely no doubt in my mind as to Mr. Caesar's heartfelt sincerity. This was obviously the most important thing that had ever happened in his life.

"We have the promise that if we sincerely confess our sins and ask for forgiveness, Jesus will wipe those sins out as completely as though they had never happened," I reassured him. "You make me happy when you say you're going to turn your life over to the Saviour. When you do, you're going to experience peace and happiness such as you have only dreamed of until now."

"I'm going to stop drinking, smoking, and gambling as of now!" Mr. Caesar declared vehemently. "I'm going to ask God to help me clean up anything else in my life that is interfering with my salvation. Can we have a word of prayer together, doctor, before I leave?" he pleaded.

"Certainly," I replied, inwardly elated that another soul had been won to Christ. "Remember, whenever you need help or guidance, ask the Lord for it in prayer. He will hear you and answer your pleas if He, in His infinite wisdom, thinks that they are for your best good."

In the next few months Mr. Caesar's life underwent a transformation that would have been incredible to anyone unacquainted with the divine power that changes men's lives. He stopped drinking and smoking, and he never let a day go by without Bible study and prayer. He began attending the church of which I was a member, and before long he was taking an active part in the Sabbath school and in other church activities. From his reading he had become convinced of the necessity of paying an honest tithe, and this he did with cheerfulness in the knowledge that he was doing the Lord's will.

The pastor and the entire congregation were in favor of accepting Caesar as a brother, after having had an opportunity of observing his sincerity and devout dedication to the Lord's work.

But threatening clouds were gathering ominously in Mr. Caesar's life. He came to my office one day, a few months after becoming active in church work, and complained of persistent pains in his abdominal region. After a thorough study of his case I decided to take a series of stomach X rays. To my horror I found that Mr. Caesar had a well-developed growth in his stomach. I hastily called a surgical conference. We decided to operate as soon as he was prepared, so I had Mr. Caesar admitted to a local hospital. However, when he had been there only a short time, I noted telltale signs that indicated unmistakably that it was cancer and that it was spreading to other parts of his body. It was too late for human aid.

As I talked and prayed with Mr. Caesar during the days that followed, I was amazed at the spirituality that had completely replaced his former worldliness. His thoughts were continually on Jesus, and his Bible was never far from his reach.

The end came about a week after his admittance to the hospital. "You know, doctor," he whispered to me, "I'm not afraid to die now. My case is in God's hands, and I know He'll take good care of me."

It was a confession of faith as simple, sincere, and heartfelt as the one given almost two thousand years ago by the repentant thief upon the cross.

My church pastor agreed to conduct the funeral services for the one for whom Christ had worked mightily to save, and there was scarcely a dry eye in the crowd at the cemetery when the service was concluded. As I was leaving, three young men approached me. "I don't think you know us, doctor," one of them began; "but we were friends of Caesar, or Al as we usually called him. He often told us about what you had done for him and how much he admired you. I want to thank you for all you did for Al. My name is George Carson, and this is Curly and Hardrock, or Hansen and Carruthers, whichever you prefer."

I shook hands with Caesar's friends and noted curiously that they all had Bibles in their hands. Apparently noticing the direction of my glance, Carson spoke up: "You know, doctor, I've read about miracles, and I've heard about miracles; but until I met Al, I'd never actually witnessed one. Al used to be a heavy drinker, a gambler, and a general all-round roisterer. He used profane language and wasn't any better than he had to be where the women were concerned. He ran a gambling layout at the barracks, and if you'd ever told me you'd find Al within a mile of any church, I'd have said you were strictly off the beam.

"Well, about three months ago," Carson continued, "Al announced out of a clear sky that he was through gambling, drinking, and smoking. We all laughed, of course, thinking it was a gag; but we soon learned differently. He threw his dice and cigarettes away; then he organized a daily Bible class among the fellows there, and he changed his life so completely he was truly a new person. It's a miracle, if I ever saw one! He passed along that book you gave him called *Steps to Christ,* so don't be too surprised if you have three more fellows seeking membership in your church before long."

As I drove back to my office I thought of how unfathomable are the ways of God in men's lives. I also breathed a fervent prayer of thankfulness that Al Caesar had found Jesus in time. His life illustrated, better than any sermon possibly could, the danger that might come from procrastination in seeking salvation.

"Seek ye the Lord." *"Now* is the day of salvation," is a warning that should be written in blazing letters where every repentant sinner might see it! For the alcoholic the message is especially meaningful, since life for him is even more uncertain and unpredictable than it is for the normal, sober person. No effort should be spared to encourage and assist the alcoholic to seek salvation *today!*

That is the most important thing I have tried to convey in this book, and if this message is taken to heart and acted upon, I will feel that all the efforts I have made are indeed worth while.

Chapter 10

Afterward

THESE, then, have been our parables. The Master Teacher used parables because of the way in which they brought home fundamental facts for men and women to hold in their minds and think on. Knowing that the Lord's pattern in all things cannot be bettered, the author has humbly told these stories.

Three things he would say in recapitulation: 1. The only sure and lasting cure for alcoholism lies in a spiritual approach to the problem. 2. Alcoholics who have stopped "trying" to overcome their drinking, and instead have turned their entire problem over to God, have achieved peace, sobriety, serenity, and happiness such as they thought impossible to attain. 3. It is equally certain that the alcoholic who stubbornly clings to the belief that he alone, or some human agency, can do this for him, is doomed to failure and to a lifetime of progressively intensifying alcoholic misery and degradation.

God's Book has said: "Incline thine ear unto wisdom, and apply thine heart to understanding; yea, if thou criest after knowledge, and liftest up thy voice for understanding; if thou seekest her as silver, and searchest for her as for hid treasures; then shalt thou understand the fear of the Lord, and find the knowledge of God." Proverbs 2:2-5.

Hunt for God. Do all of the things that a believer would do, praying and living with the ideals of service which mark a believer. Ask God constantly to reveal Himself to you. Ask God to take over your life. Each day read your Bible. Enroll in the free introductory correspondence Bible course for alcoholics. Join a Bible study group. Don't worry if God's truths do not come to you suddenly. Some have had that experience, but many more have found God because they offered themselves to Him and hunted for Him. Al Caesar found Him that way.

SPECIAL HELPS

The following supplementary reading is strongly recommended as a "must" for the alcoholic patient seeking permanent sobriety:

Introductory Bible Lessons for Alcoholics

This free Bible correspondence course, prepared by the author of this book, is now available for alcoholics and their friends by writing to the publishers of this book.

The studies demonstrate clearly the spiritual methods by which alcoholism can be permanently overcome. This course offers a simple, easily understood study of the Book of books.

A copy of *The Prophecies of Daniel and the Revelation* is also available through the publishers, the Pacific Press Publishing Association, Mountain View, California.

David Dare, by Earle A. Rowell.

This book is the most popular publication with the

alcoholic patients in Los Angeles's alcoholic rehabilitation clinic. It has been instrumental in laying the groundwork for the full acceptance of Christ and a belief in the Holy Scriptures. Copies of *David Dare* may be obtained from the publishers of this book.

Steps to Christ, by Ellen G. White.

The opening chapters of this outstanding book tell vividly of God's love for man and of the sinner's need of Christ. It outlines in detail the steps necessary for the alcoholic to follow in order to grow in Christian grace and thereby achieve permanent sobriety and spiritual happiness and serenity. Copies of *Steps to Christ* may be obtained from the above-mentioned publishers.

Your Home and Health, by Ellen G. White.

This is a book for every home where there is an alcoholic problem. It lists the basic principles of healthful living so necessary to obtaining permanent sobriety. It has 380 pages of vital information for alcoholics and is liberally illustrated. Full information concerning this book may be secured by writing to the publishers, the Pacific Press Publishing Association, Mountain View, California.